LESLIE DIENES
Department of Geography

W9-AGX-878

USSR Agriculture
Atlas

CENTRAL INTELLIGENCE AGENCY

DECEMBER 1974

Table of Contents

Preface

This atlas provides information on the complexities of agriculture in the USSR, one of the world's major food producers. The food-producing capabilities of this giant land are extremely important as food shortages threaten many parts of the world and as international commodity trade assumes increasing economic and political significance.

Comparisons with U.S. agriculture are intended to help make the information on the Soviet Union meaningful by placing it in a familiar context. Such comparisons are necessarily imperfect because Soviet and U.S. data are based on different definitions and collection procedures.

The atlas draws on many sources, including numerous excellent studies by Soviet geographers and agronomists, statistical publications and official reports of the Soviet Government, and the extensive research and analytical efforts of U.S. Government officials and of American students of Soviet agriculture.

Some geographic names have been simplified from the form designated by the U.S. Board on Geographic Names (BGN). The BGN-approved names are listed on the inside back cover.

Agriculture's Role in the Economy

Agricultural production has a much greater impact on overall economic performance in the USSR than in the United States. Although the farm sector's proportional contribution to gross national product (GNP) has been falling rapidly, USSR agriculture still accounts for more than one-fifth of the Soviet GNP and employs more than one-quarter of the labor force. In the United States, on the other hand, agriculture contributes less than 4 percent of GNP and employs only 5 percent of the labor force.

Year-to-year fluctuations in farm output make it difficult to maintain an uninterrupted rise in Soviet living standards. The effect of failure to meet food production goals is magnified because food accounts for nearly 50 percent of the total consumption of goods and services and because carryover stocks are generally inadequate. In the United States, in contrast, food products make up less than one-fifth of total consumption, the growth of farm output has been rela-

tively steady, and stocks have been adequate to cushion minor variations in production.

Soviet agriculture is now a major recipient of investment funds, reflecting the high priority given it by the leadership. Since 1965, the share of the nation's investment (productive and non-productive) allocated to agriculture has averaged 25 percent, compared with less than 20 percent in the preceding decade. The current Five-Year Plan (1971-75) calls for investment in agriculture of nearly 129 billion rubles. Meeting this goal will require increased agricultural investment averaging 9½ percent annually; agriculture's share of total investment would then rise to 27½ percent. Two-thirds of the way through the Plan, progress toward the goal remains on schedule.

The plan for total investment in machinery and equipment for farms during 1971-75 is 35½ billion rubles, a 54 percent increase over the previous 5-year period. About

one-fifth of the total investment in agriculture is to be expended on land amelioration, mostly reclamation by irrigation and drainage. This is expected to result in an expansion of about 30 percent in irrigated and drained land.

Large future requirements for capital investment in agriculture are apparent in the official goals. The goals call for (1) "optimum" machinery parks in agriculture, (2) specialization of livestock production, (3) construction of adequate granaries, elevators, and other product storage facilities, and (4) expansion of land amelioration programs. As part of the latter effort, Brezhnev announced in December 1973 a 15-year land improvement program for the non-chernozem region of the Russian Republic. The program calls for reclamation or improvement of 50 million hectares—32 million of cropland (about 15 percent of current sown area) and 18 million of grazing land.

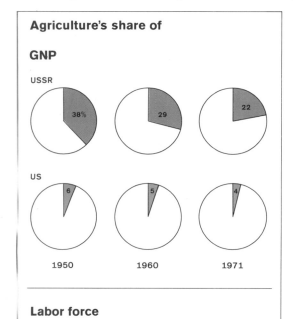

Agriculture's share of

GNP

USSR — 1950: 38%; 1960: 29; 1971: 22

US — 1950: 6; 1960: 5; 1971: 4

Labor force

USSR — 1950: 54%; 1960: 42; 1971: 29

US — 1950: 15; 1960: 10; 1971: 5

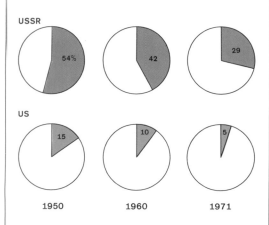

Total investment

USSR — 1965: 22%; 1970: 24; 1975 (planned): 28

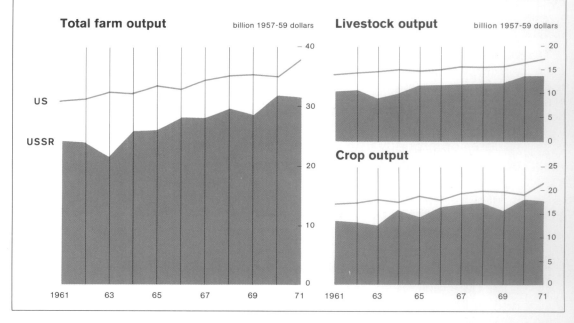

Total farm output — billion 1957-59 dollars

US / USSR — 1961–71 (scale 0–40)

Livestock output — billion 1957-59 dollars (scale 0–20)

Crop output (scale 0–25)

1961, 63, 65, 67, 69, 71

Number of persons supported by one farm worker

USSR: 7

US: 46

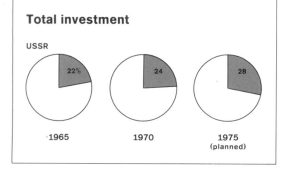

Commodity Trade

The Soviet Union is normally a net importer of agricultural commodities. Soviet agricultural imports have grown at about the same rate as other imports, remaining at one-fifth of the total. Agricultural exports, on the other hand, have not kept pace, dropping from 21 percent of total exports in 1960 to 11 percent in 1972, a decrease largely attributable to the relative stagnation of grain exports. U.S. agricultural trade follows an entirely different pattern, with agricultural imports accounting for 12 percent and agricultural exports 19 percent of their respective totals.

The USSR's major agricultural exports are grain and plant fibers (largely cotton), while major imports are grain, fibers (cotton and wool), and unrefined sugar. Some vegetables, fruit, and berries are also imported. Thus the USSR is in the unusual position of both exporting and importing large amounts of grain and cotton, mainly because of trade obligations to client states and trade in different grades or types of the same commodity.

The Soviet Union's largest trading partners for agricultural commodities—as with total trade—are the Communist countries. Since 1960, about 70 percent of total agricultural exports have gone to the Communist countries, which earns the USSR no hard currency. On the other hand, more than half of the USSR's agricultural imports in recent years have originated in the West, and a large part of this must be paid for in hard currency. For example, the nearly $2 billion of grain imported in 1972-73 contributed significantly to the record Soviet hard currency trade deficits, which were financed by gold sales, 3-year CCC credits, and some short-term borrowing.

Since 1960, the most dynamic sector of Soviet agricultural trade has been its grain imports. A disastrous harvest in 1963 reversed the traditional Soviet role of net grain exporter. A poor harvest in 1972 again forced the USSR to import record quantities of grain. This time, however, the decision to spend large amounts of hard currency also reflected a change in agricultural and consumer policy. The 1965 Brezhnev agricultural program to provide more meat and other quality foods stimulated the domestic demand for grain as livestock feed, while the use of grain for food hardly changed. By 1969-70, grain output had fallen behind the increased demand, making necessary deep inroads into government reserves. The massive grain imports of 1972 were essential to maintain the livestock goals. More than half of these imports consisted of wheat, apparently intended to replace the domestic wheat fed to livestock because of its poor milling quality. Wheat was also a better buy on the world market than corn or other feedgrains.

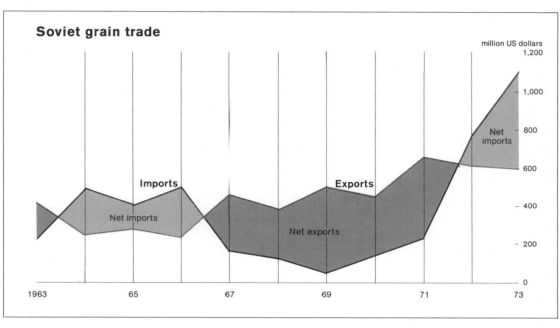

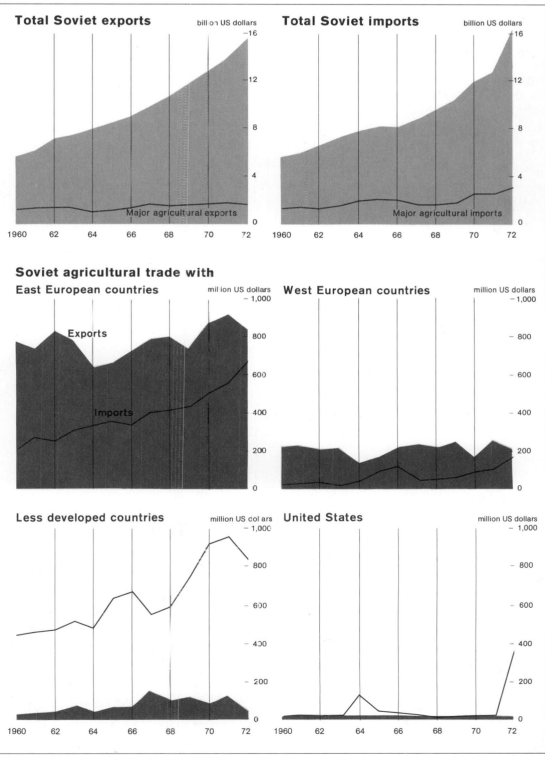

Policy Issues

Agriculture is vitally important to the domestic economy of the USSR, and it is a way of life for a large though diminishing segment of the Soviet citizenry. In recent years, agriculture has also taken on vastly increased international political and economic importance to the Soviet Union as the nation's role in international agricultural commodity trade has expanded significantly.

Most of the agricultural land of the USSR is climatically comparable to Canada and North Central United States. On the whole, the farmland of the USSR is less productive than that of the United States because of environmental limitations. Even with a larger area under crops, production is less.

Of the three elements essential to plant growth—heat, moisture, and nutrients—the supply of heat is the least amenable to improvement over any large area like the USSR. Most Soviet land is heat-deficient in terms of agricultural requirements. Hothouse agriculture is expanding, but it is a specialized capital-intensive development. Improvement of the ability of plants to withstand cold, through selective breeding, is the most promising means of extending agriculture or improving yields in colder areas.

Moisture deficiency is also a major problem in the USSR. Although drought-resistant varieties of plants are being developed and dryfarming techniques improved, the most effective response to moisture deficiency remains the age-old technique of irrigation. Irrigation has increased production in the comparatively warm steppe and desert areas of the USSR and plans call for further rapid extension. However, large amounts of both capital and labor are required and in some areas benefits are difficult to sustain because of soil deterioration.

The Soviet Union has some comparatively good soils, but natural soil fertility supplies only a part of plant nutrient requirements. Good matching of soil and crop, skillful crop rotation practices, and large quantities of organic and mineral fertilizers and of trace elements are necessary.

Soviet agriculture has come a long way despite environmental limitations and the disruptions caused by revolution, collectivization, and the dislocations of World War II. The increasing population—now more than 250 million—has been fed adequately in recent decades, and the diet of most Soviet citizens has improved. Although the amount of agricultural land per capita has declined, more and better food has been available because yields have been increased for most of the major crops. This has been accomplished despite inefficiencies in the Soviet farm system and lagging agricultural technology.

Tasks still facing the farm sector are many and will pose difficult choices for the Soviet leadership through the 1970's and beyond. They include:

- Making adequate capital available for investment in agriculture;
- Acquiring new technology and applying it effectively throughout the country;
- Correcting imbalances in the regional agricultural labor supply and raising the low level of technical skills;
- Correcting continuing inefficiencies in the organization and management of farm work; and
- Coping with consumer pressures for more and better food and with pressures for improving rural living conditions.

Commitments to the consumer have heavily influenced the USSR's trade decisions in recent years. For example, grain purchases from the United States from 1972 to 1974 kept bread supplies and quality at adequate levels, and the purchase of low-priced meat on the world market in 1974 helped satisfy growing consumer demand without depleting livestock inventories required under the long-term plan to increase Soviet meat production.

Since the benefits of recent improvements in technology have yet to be fully realized, the USSR appears to be in a position to keep pace with the food requirements of a population whose rate of growth has already slowed. A considerable gap remains between what the vast agricultural lands of the country can produce and what they do produce. If this gap is closed, the USSR may be able both to feed its own population and to help ease world food problems. But this would require difficult choices. Would the USSR be willing to participate in an international reserve system that would require disclosure of current information on cereals production and reserve stocks? Also, how would the USSR choose between boosting the production of livestock feed to increase meat supplies at home and exporting food grain to foreign areas where it is sorely needed?

The USSR is almost 2.5 times as large as the United States. Climatic conditions are generally analogous to areas in Canada and the north central Plains states.

Comparative area and latitude

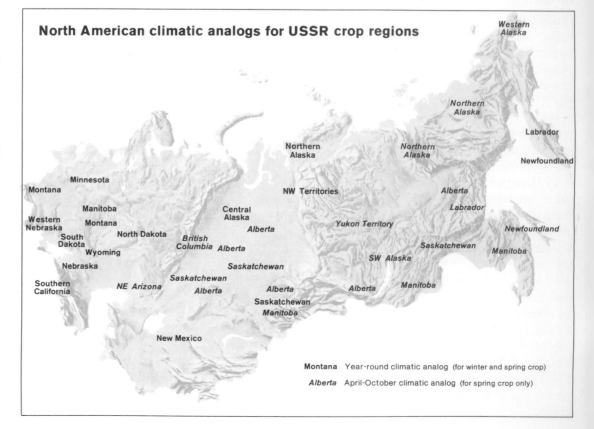

North American climatic analogs for USSR crop regions

Montana Year-round climatic analog (for winter and spring crop)

Alberta April-October climatic analog (for spring crop only)

 Part 1

Environment

Environmental conditions in the USSR are far from the best for agriculture. While the natural endowment permits farming over large areas of the country, productive cropland is constrained on the north by cold and on the south by aridity. Extension of farming beyond this agricultural zone is a risky and expensive undertaking.

The growing season in most of the Soviet Union is short compared with that in most U.S. agricultural regions. Late frosts and early snows are common in the major grain growing areas, which lie at the same latitudes as the prairie provinces of Canada. Areas warm enough to foster plant growth tend to suffer from moisture deficiency; and semi-desert and desert conditions predominate in the southernmost part of the USSR, which lies at the same latitude as Tennessee.

The variability of the weather from year to year makes it difficult to maintain steady growth in agricultural production. Hazardous weather conditions frequently diminish yields and in some areas valuable crops are lost entirely because of drought and desiccating winds, violent thunderstorms, and hail. Winterkill occurs each year, and in some years it is extensive.

The natural assets of the USSR include the most extensive agricultural land resources of any country in the world. In addition, the range and diversity of the USSR's agroclimatic regions make possible the production of a wide variety of crops. Another major asset is the broad belt of fertile chernozem (black earth) soil which extends from the western border far beyond the Urals. Although much of the country has no agricultural potential because of rugged terrain or extreme cold, there remain areas which may some day become productive with the aid of advanced technology.

Zone of agriculture

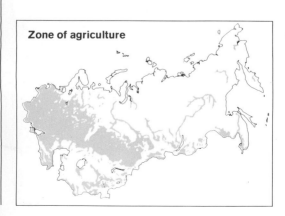

Thermal Resources

More than 30 percent of the USSR is too cold for agriculture, and an additional 40 percent is so cold that only hardy early-maturing crops can be grown. (In contrast, cold is a limiting factor in about 20 percent of the United States.) Only in the southern USSR does the available warmth permit a wide range of crops; other factors, such as moisture and economic considerations, determine what crops are planted.

Most crops develop best when the average daily temperatures remain above 10°C. Soviet scientists express the heat supply numerically by the so-called "sum of temperatures," which is the total number of degrees by which average daily temperatures during the growing season exceed 10°C. If the temperature sum is insufficient during the growing period, plants will fail to mature even though their moisture and nutrient requirements are met.

Agroclimatologists have measured in this manner the heat supply available throughout the USSR in order to evaluate the crop potential of various regions. Each crop has its own requirements for warmth. Some strains of barley, for example, can mature in areas where the temperature sum during the growing period is as low as 800 degrees. Thus, barley cultivation can extend into the northernmost parts of the country. On the other hand, corn for grain requires at least twice that amount of heat and preferably more. Its cultivation is restricted to areas where temperatures are moderate to warm, where it may be in competition with other important crops for the available land.

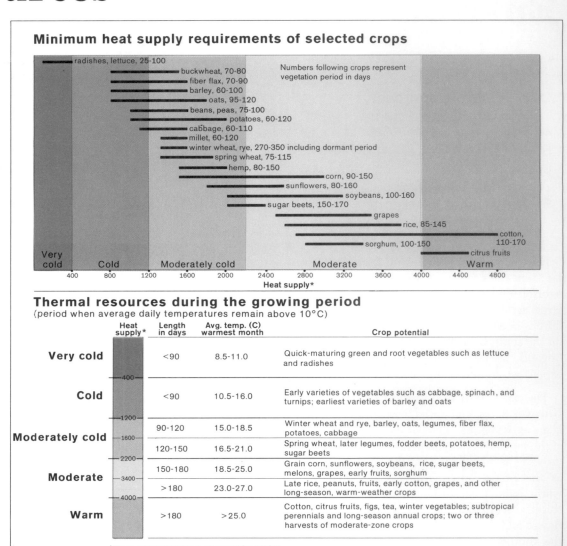

Minimum heat supply requirements of selected crops

Numbers following crops represent vegetation period in days

radishes, lettuce, 25-100
buckwheat, 70-80
fiber flax, 70-90
barley, 60-100
oats, 95-120
beans, peas, 75-100
potatoes, 60-120
cabbage, 60-110
millet, 60-120
winter wheat, rye, 270-350 including dormant period
spring wheat, 75-115
hemp, 80-150
corn, 90-150
sunflowers, 80-160
soybeans, 100-160
sugar beets, 150-170
grapes
rice, 85-145
cotton, 110-170
sorghum, 100-150
citrus fruits

Very cold | Cold | Moderately cold | Moderate | Warm

400 800 1200 1600 2000 2400 2800 3200 3600 4000 4400 4800

Heat supply*

Thermal resources during the growing period
(period when average daily temperatures remain above 10°C)

	Heat supply*	Length in days	Avg. temp. (C) warmest month	Crop potential
Very cold		<90	8.5-11.0	Quick-maturing green and root vegetables such as lettuce and radishes
	400			
Cold		<90	10.5-16.0	Early varieties of vegetables such as cabbage, spinach, and turnips; earliest varieties of barley and oats
	1200			
Moderately cold	1600	90-120	15.0-18.5	Winter wheat and rye, barley, oats, legumes, fiber flax, potatoes, cabbage
	2200	120-150	16.5-21.0	Spring wheat, later legumes, fodder beets, potatoes, hemp, sugar beets
Moderate	3400	150-180	18.5-25.0	Grain corn, sunflowers, soybeans, rice, sugar beets, melons, grapes, early fruits, sorghum
	4000	>180	23.0-27.0	Late rice, peanuts, fruits, early cotton, grapes, and other long-season, warm-weather crops
Warm		>180	>25.0	Cotton, citrus fruits, figs, tea, winter vegetables; subtropical perennials and long-season annual crops; two or three harvests of moderate-zone crops

*Sums of temperatures above 10°C (50°F)

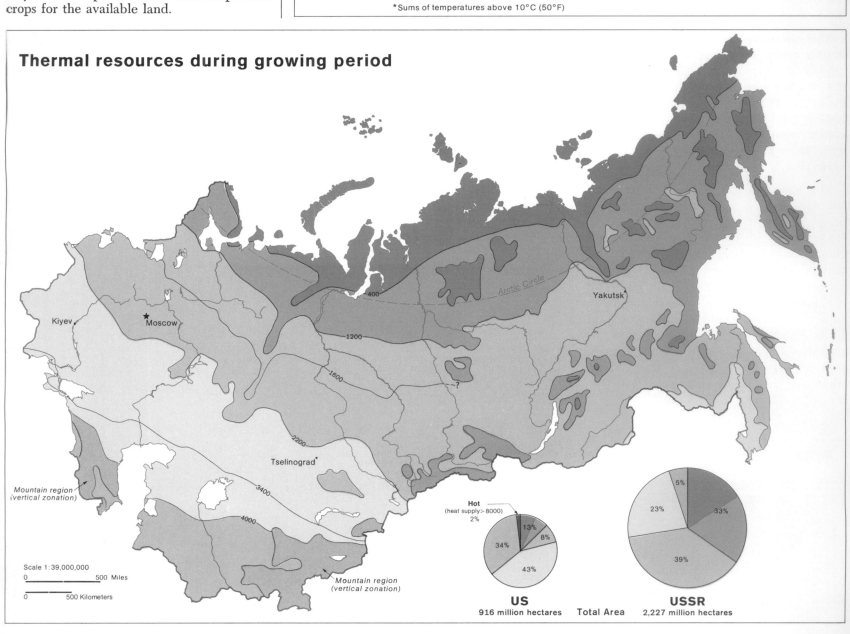

Thermal resources during growing period

Kiyev
Moscow
Arctic Circle
Yakutsk
400
1200
1600
?
Tselinograd
2000
3400
4000

Mountain region (vertical zonation)

Mountain region (vertical zonation)

Scale 1:39,000,000

0   500 Miles

0   500 Kilometers

Hot
(heat supply>8000)
2%

13%
8%
34%
43%

US
916 million hectares

Total Area

5%
23%
33%
39%

USSR
2,227 million hectares

Moisture Resources

More than half the arable land in the USSR lacks adequate and reliable moisture. Consequently, it is necessary to employ agricultural techniques aimed at bringing moisture conditions closer to the optimum for farming. Irrigation, dryfarming, planting of shelterbelts, runoff and erosion control, and snow retention all stem from the need to conserve and increase soil moisture. The United States has similar problem areas in the Great Plains and the West.

The well watered half of the USSR is mostly unsuitable for farming because the growing season is too short and too cold. Even where there is sufficient warmth, excessive moisture, under certain soil and terrain conditions, can lead to drainage problems and reduced yields. In the United States, similar problems occur in the East and in the northern Pacific coastal area.

Moisture supply is commonly measured as the ratio of annual precipitation to potential evaporation. Precipitation alone is an inadequate index of available moisture because high temperatures, low humidity, and strong winds can reduce the benefits of rainfall by causing rapid evaporation and transpiration. Conversely, with low temperatures and high humidity even light precipitation is adequate for plant growth.

Moisture zones		Probability that year will be:				
		Excessively wet	Wet	Moderately dry	Dry	Semi-arid to arid
Sufficient	Excessively wet	64%	20%	15%	1%	
	Wet	30%	32%	33%	5%	
Inadequate	Moderately dry	4%	16%	57%	19%	4%
	Dry		1%	21%	49%	29%
Negligible	Semi-arid			1%	24%	75%
	Arid				2%	98%

1.33
1.00
0.55
0.33
0.22

*Moisture value = annual precipitation / potential evaporation

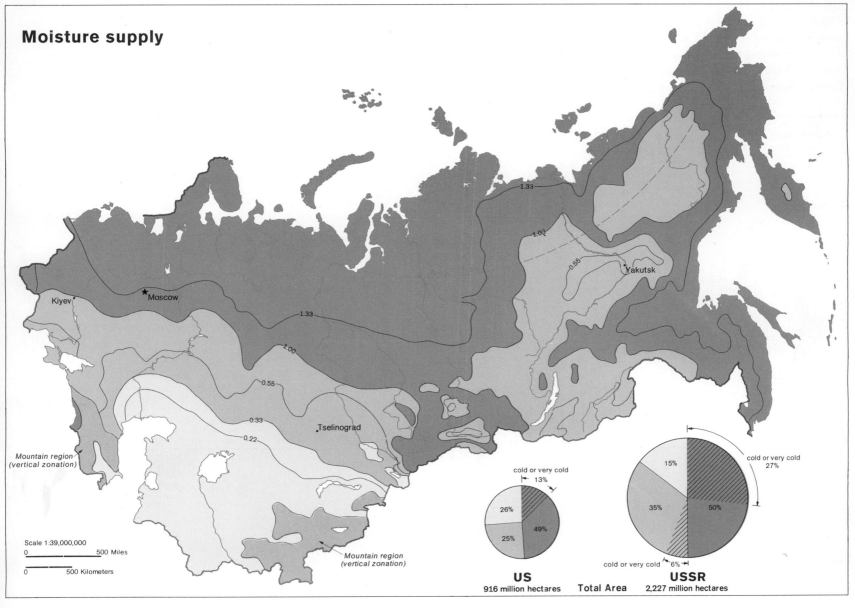

Moisture supply

Kiyev · ★Moscow · Yakutsk · Tselinograd

1.33 · 1.00 · 0.55 · 0.33 · 0.22

Mountain region (vertical zonation)

Scale 1:39,000,000

0 ——— 500 Miles

0 ——— 500 Kilometers

US
916 million hectares
cold or very cold 13%
26% · 25% · 49%

Total Area

USSR
2,227 million hectares
cold or very cold 27%
15% · 35% · 50%
cold or very cold 6%

Wintering Conditions

Winter crops in the USSR are especially vulnerable when snow cover is lacking or is thin. Winterkill—caused largely by intense cold, icing, thawing and refreezing, heaving, or drought—is a frequent hazard to winter grain. Tree crops, berries, and other hibernating crops can also be damaged by severe winter conditions. On the other hand, deep snow on the fields provides protection from wind and cold and assures better soil moisture reserves in the spring.

The character of winter in the USSR varies from unrelenting and bitter cold in Siberia to changeable and warm in the Caucasus; for most of the country it is a long, cold season with a persistent snow cover. The severest conditions prevail in the Yakut ASSR, where winter lasts 7 to 9 months, snow cover remains all winter from the first snowfall, and temperatures as low as −71°C have been recorded. Wintering conditions moderate westward and southward. In northern European USSR the season is a month or two shorter and less severe, but the snow cover is deeper (in some lowland areas more than 1 meter) and more compact.

In central and southern European USSR, where winter grain is an important crop, winter generally lasts about 4 or 5 months, but its severity changes from year to year. When intrusions of cold air from the Arctic or Siberia prevail, winters are cold and snowy, and temperatures can drop to levels that damage winter crops and fruit trees. When westerly marine air masses dominate, winter weather is warmer and overcast, with wet snow, sometimes even rain. Intermittent freezing and thawing makes the snow cover irregular in depth and density and can result in the formation of damaging ice crusts.

The Caucasus coast of the Black Sea is the warmest part of the USSR in winter. Only January and February can be considered winter months, and even then temperatures average above freezing. There is usually no snow, but occasional cold waves from the north or east bring snow and frost that damage citrus and other subtropical plants.

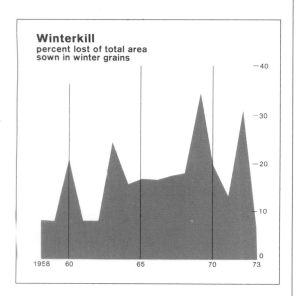

Winterkill
percent lost of total area
sown in winter grains

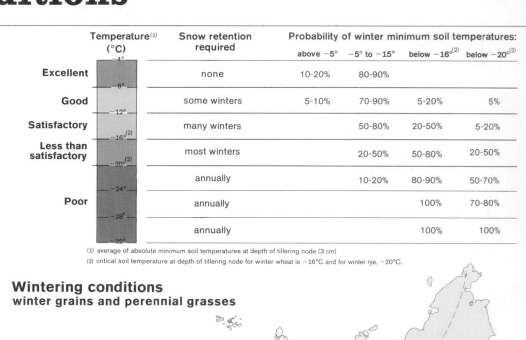

	Temperature[1] (°C)	Snow retention required	Probability of winter minimum soil temperatures:			
			above −5°	−5° to −15°	below −16°[2]	below −20°[2]
Excellent		none	10-20%	80-90%		
Good		some winters	5-10%	70-90%	5-20%	5%
Satisfactory		many winters		50-80%	20-50%	5-20%
Less than satisfactory		most winters		20-50%	50-80%	20-50%
		annually		10-20%	80-90%	50-70%
Poor		annually			100%	70-80%
		annually			100%	100%

(1) average of absolute minimum soil temperatures at depth of tillering node (3 cm)
(2) critical soil temperature at depth of tillering node for winter wheat is −16°C and for winter rye, −20°C.

Wintering conditions
winter grains and perennial grasses

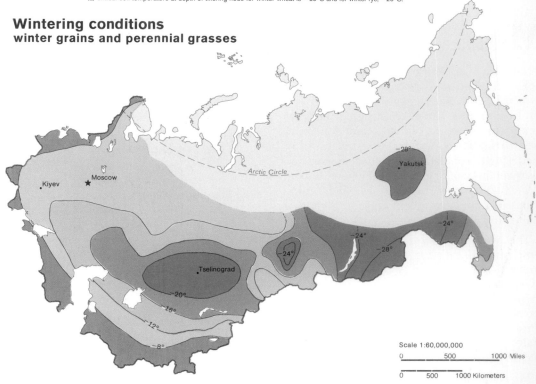

Scale 1:60,000,000
0   500   1000 Miles
0   500   1000 Kilometers

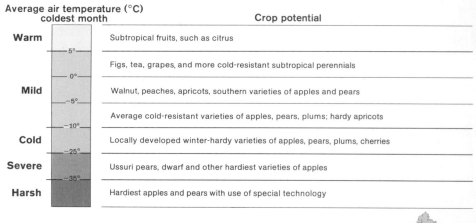

	Average air temperature (°C) coldest month	Crop potential
Warm		Subtropical fruits, such as citrus
		Figs, tea, grapes, and more cold-resistant subtropical perennials
Mild		Walnut, peaches, apricots, southern varieties of apples and pears
		Average cold-resistant varieties of apples, pears, plums; hardy apricots
Cold		Locally developed winter-hardy varieties of apples, pears, plums, cherries
Severe		Ussuri pears, dwarf and other hardiest varieties of apples
Harsh		Hardiest apples and pears with use of special technology

Wintering conditions
tree crops and berries

Scale 1:60,000,000
0   500   1000 Miles
0   500   1000 Kilometers

Snow

Snow cover	Depth (cm)	Duration (days)	Meliorative measures
None or very thin, intermittent	<10	<80	None, impractical
Year-to-year variability, unpredictable depth and duration	10-40	40-160	Snow retention and accumulation measures used to shelter crops and to improve moisture reserves
Thin to moderate, frequent melting	20-40	60-120	Occasional removal of early-winter deep-snow to induce soil freezing and winter rest period in crop growth
Moderate depth and duration	30-60	100-180	In west, occasional deep-snow removal to prevent smothering and waterlogging of crops; in east, snow retention to protect crops
Moderate depth, long lasting	30-50	>200	Occasional inducement of early-spring melting to extend pasturing and growing season
Deep, long lasting	>60	160-240	In west, occasional deep-snow removal to prevent smothering and waterlogging of crops

Snow cover conditions

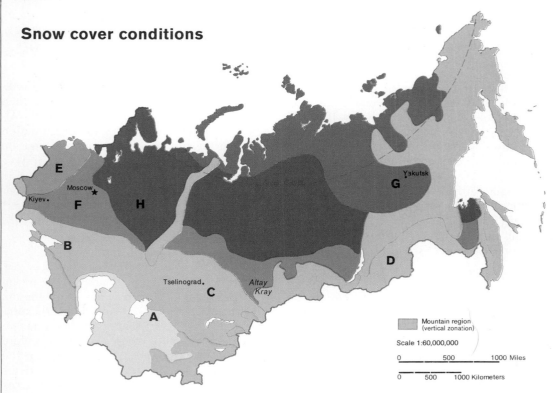

Mountain region (vertical zonation)

Scale 1:60,000,000

0   500   1000 Miles

0   500   1000 Kilometers

Snow calendars

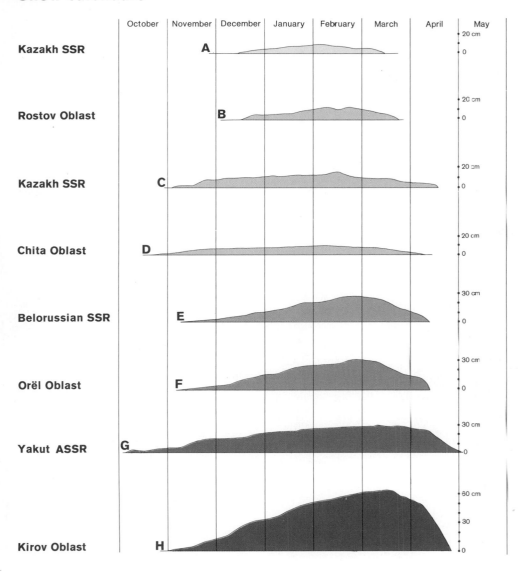

Nearly all of the USSR is covered by snow in winter, but depth and duration vary from region to region and from year to year. Soviet experts note that the snow depth should be at least 30 cm in European USSR and 40 cm in Siberia to protect winter plantings from the very low temperatures. Snow retention measures to protect fields and to enhance moisture reserves are carried out over an area of 50 to 60 million hectares, mostly in Kazakhstan and Siberia. The principal technique is to accumulate and hold the snow by placing obstructions on the fields at right angles to the prevailing winds. Commonly used obstructions include removable fences, high stubble, rows of corn, sunflower or mustard stalks, snow ridges, straw mulch, brush piles, and plowed earth ridges. Forest strips are also effective for snow retention over large areas. Excessively deep snow is removed by plows or is compacted on the fields. To hasten snow melting, darkening materials such as soot, peat dust, or ashes are sprinkled on the surface.

Snow ridges being constructed in Altay Kray to retain moisture

Precipitation

Precipitation is moderate to light over most of the USSR's agricultural lands. Prevailing westerly winds from the ocean bring moisture into the European USSR but become progressively drier as they move eastward and southeastward. The wettest part of the country is in the Caucasus—a small area along the coast and mountain slopes facing the prevailing winds from the Black Sea. Here, up to 3,900 mm of precipitation has been recorded in a single year.

▨ Moderate precipitation

Because of their relative proximity to the marine moisture source, the western regions have fairly reliable, moderate precipitation with a favorable seasonal distribution. The maximum amount occurs—usually as frequent light rain or showers—during the short, warm June-August period, when days are long and plant growth is rapid. Since evaporation rates are low and dry weather is fairly rare, rainfall is sufficient to maintain soil moisture reserves. Occasionally the rain is heavy, and thunderstorms occur 10 to 20 times in summer. During the winter there are numerous light snowstorms.

In the Far East, precipitation is associated with onshore monsoons, and annual amounts are usually sufficient for maintaining good soil moisture reserves. The heaviest rains generally occur in late summer, causing problems at harvest time. During the offshore monsoons in winter, snowfall is very light.

▨ Light and variable precipitation

Precipitation is markedly deficient in the steppes of southern European USSR, which stretch from the Ukraine and the north Caucasus through the lower Volga basin into southwestern Siberia. Problems are similar to those of the Great Plains of the United States: rainfall is light, variable from year to year, and unpredictable. Because the average is barely sufficient to support crop growth, variations downward are more serious than in the more humid regions to the north. Although the greater part of the precipitation falls during the growing season, evaporation is high, there is little soil moisture reserve to sustain plants through dry periods, and the threat of crop losses is ever-present. Rainstorms, sometimes heavy and often of short duration, may be accompanied by squalls and hail.

▢ Scanty precipitation

In the Central Asia lowlands there are no dependable rain-bearing winds at any season. The heart of the desert area is nearly rainless and cloudless in summer. Showers are rare, and sometimes rain evaporates before reaching the ground. Precipitation in the mountains to the southeast feeds rivers that supply water to irrigated farming areas in the lowlands.

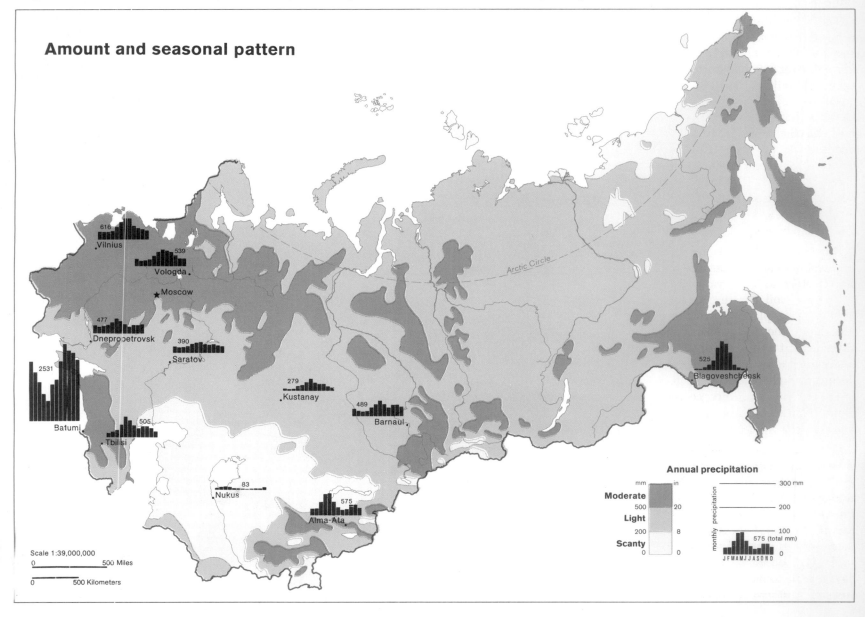

Amount and seasonal pattern

Weather Hazards

The weather of the USSR is subject to rapid, extreme, and damaging fluctuations. Drought and crop failure are recorded repeatedly throughout the agricultural history of Russia and the USSR. The regions most often and most severely affected are also the best natural grain-producing areas in the country, which explains the importance and urgency that Soviet agricultural specialists attach to drought control and the development of new high-yield, drought-resistant crop varieties.

Adverse weather was the primary cause of the poor harvest in 1972 that forced the USSR to import record quantities of grain. That year an unusually severe, snow-deficient winter was followed by an extraordinarily hot, dry summer that reduced agricultural production over much of the southern half of European USSR. Winterkill affected more than 30 percent of the area sown in winter grains, making extensive re-sowing necessary. Severe drought from mid-June to August—when temperatures rose to 30°-35°C for several days in succession and precipitation was only 30 to 40 percent of normal—withered crops and dried up pastures. Yields dropped sharply.

The same large-scale atmospheric conditions that produce droughts in one area cause other weather anomalies, such as unseasonable frost, severe winter cold, or persistent rains, elsewhere. For example, during the summer of 1972, when European USSR was unusually hot and dry, the Soviet Far East was unusually cold and rainy, and many farms were flooded.

The drought-prone areas are also the regions commonly affected by the dry, hot, easterly or southeasterly winds called *sukhovey*. Strongest and most frequent over the open, generally flat steppes, these winds can occur several days a month from April to October but are most frequent in summer at a time when crops are ripening. During a *sukhovey* the relative humidity falls below 30 percent, winds fluctuate from about 8 to nearly 50 kilometers (5-30 miles) per hour, and temperatures range from 25°C to 40°C. These hot dry winds last from a few hours to several days.

Damage to plants is usually quick and irreparable, but its magnitude depends on such factors as crop variety, phase of development, soil moisture, and *sukhovey* intensity. Most plants are not able to adapt quickly to the sharp changes in their environment at the onset of a *sukhovey*. The desiccating effect is more intense than that during drought because the high temperatures and low humidity continue day and night. Plants are not able to "rest" and restore their turgor.

Drought is not the only weather problem in southern European USSR. The heavy local rainstorms and hail that frequently accompany thunderstorms can create difficulties several times during the growing season. In the Caucasus, hailstorms often cause serious damage to orchards and vineyards. Hail occurs on an average of 9 to 12 days a year, compared to 1 to 3 days in other areas of southern European USSR.

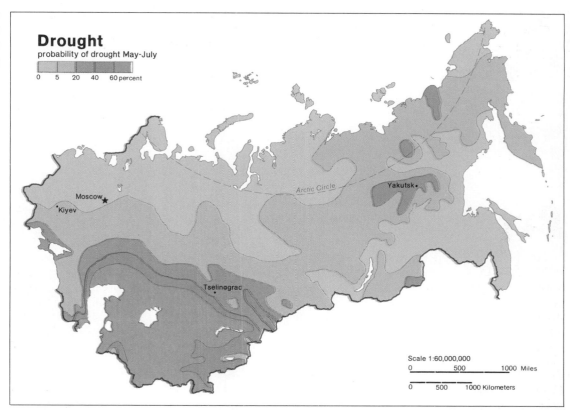

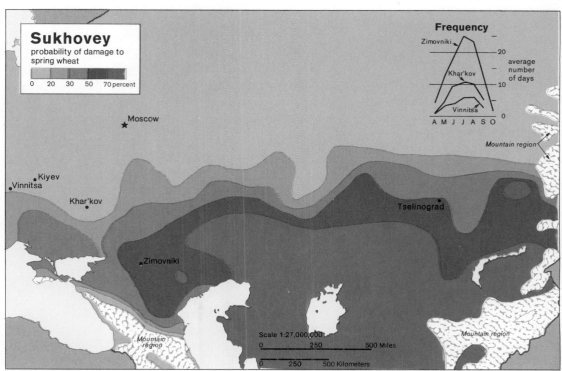

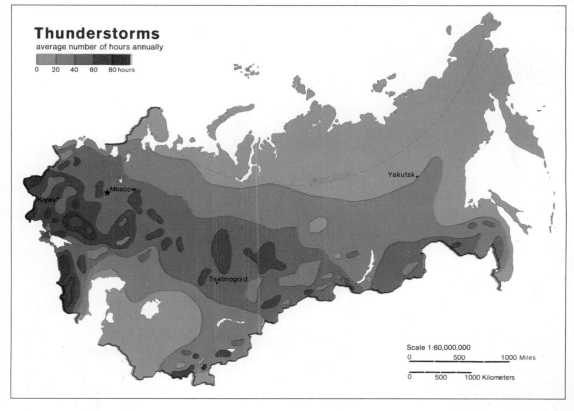

Stormy Weather, 1973

11 August: Disturbance develops into intense storm with heavy, widespread rainfall

13 August: Storm joins approaching polar front

Stormy weather created problems for harvesting in 1973. Favorable early summer weather, which caused grain crops in the European USSR to grow exceptionally tall and heavily laden with kernels—and therefore very susceptible to lodging (flattening)—was followed by frequent thunderstorms and frontal passages from the end of June to the completion of the harvest in October. The associated winds and heavy rain lodged much of the grain crop, particularly in the winter grain belt. By mid-July Soviet newspapers were reporting that more than 17 percent (2,500,000 hectares) of the Ukrainian grain crop had already been flattened.

One meteorological event in this sequence was of particular interest

because of its size and intensity. On 7 August an atmospheric disturban developed over the eastern Black Sea. The circulation aloft was favorable f the deepening of this disturbance, and a high-pressure area west of the Ura prevented it from moving quickly eastward, away from the source of moistur Cold temperatures at the upper level made convective activity unusual vigorous.

By 11 August the disturbance had developed into an intense storm affectin the area from the Black Sea northward to Moscow and eastward to Sarato Rain was heavy and widespread. More than 100 mm—double the avera rainfall for the entire month of August—was reported in western Kursk Oble

14 August: Record rainfall continues near Moscow; weather improves to south

17 August: Scattered precipitation persists

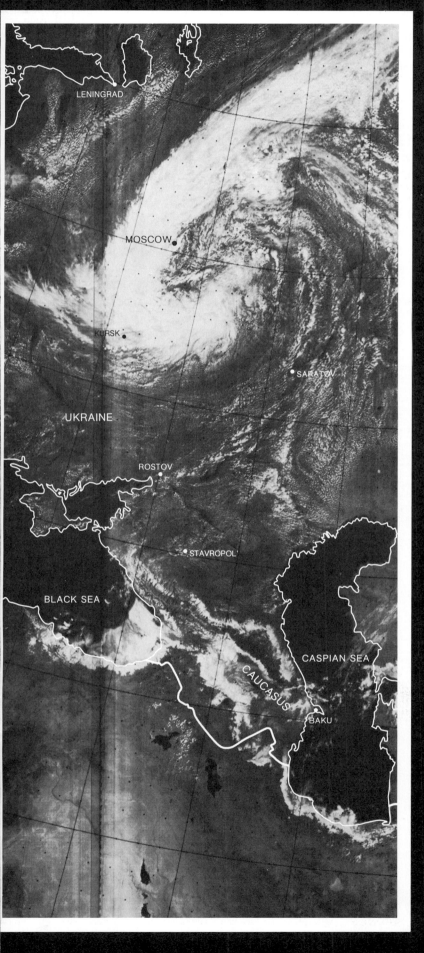

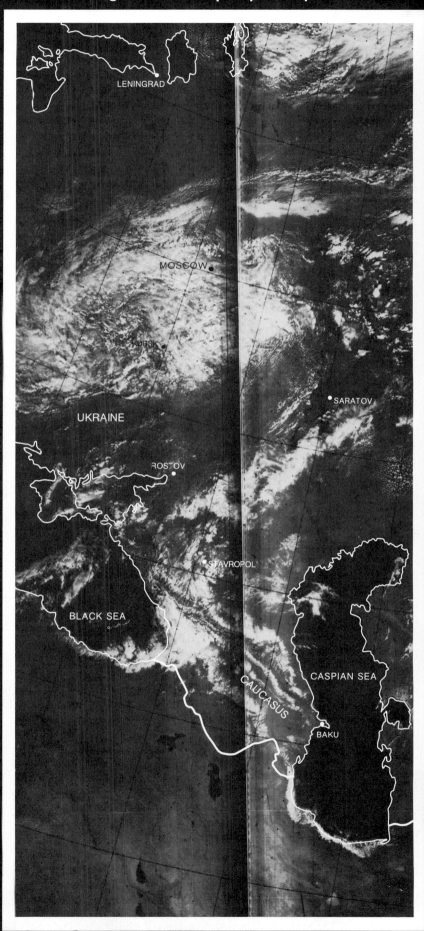

d southern Stavropol' Kray. Winds reached 20 to 30 knots.

The storm seemed to abate on 12 August but picked up new impetus on the th and 14th as it joined an approaching polar front. By 14 August the center the storm was southeast of Moscow. Weather improved in the eastern raine and northern Caucasus, but near Moscow rain fell in record amounts, aling 150 to 160 mm for the month, equalled only twice in the last century. attered precipitation persisted until about 17 August.

The almost daily heavy rains and high winds flattened and tangled the ain. Cutting swaths and combining became difficult, and rain-saturated soil ther slowed operations. Grain rotted and sometimes germinated in the

swaths, and that which arrived at state procurement centers often had an unacceptably high moisture content. Special attachments designed to recover lodged grain were fitted to the machines, and in drastic cases the crop was harvested by hand. The quality of grain stored in the open, due to a shortage of adequate storage facilities, was also adversely affected.

In the central chernozem zone, where the storm caused the most damage, the harvesting scheduled to be completed in mid-August was still under way at the end of September. Preparations for the 1974 season—fallow plowing for the spring crops and the sowing of winter crops—were critically delayed as well.

Photos from Defense Meteorology Satellite Program

Soils

The most important agricultural soils in the USSR are the chernozems, the naturally fertile black earth that stretches from the Ukraine to beyond the Urals. Like their counterparts in the prairies of North America, the Russian chernozems were formed under grasslands vegetation in semiarid conditions and have a thick upper layer rich in organic matter and nitrogen.

Chernozem and chestnut soils—the latter slightly less fertile—cover only 13 percent of the USSR area but account for more than 60 percent of the arable land. These soils have abundant mineral and organic nutrients, although the less productive meadow chernozem and light chestnut soils may require soil additives for maximum productivity. No other soils are as suitable for soil-exhausting crops such as wheat, corn, and sugar beets. Despite their many favorable characteristics, both the chernozem and chestnut soils are vulnerable to erosion and moisture deficiency.

Gray and brown forest soils, located north of the chernozem zone, have excellent soil structures and with careful soil management and proper application of fertilizers can be made quite productive. These soils have been cultivated extensively since the early days of Russian history. Poor conservation practices have led to serious erosion problems in many localities, but these soils and their northern neighbors, the more acid turfy-podzolic soils,

have in some areas been considerably improved through land reclamation and soil treatment programs.

Sierozem (gray earth) soils of Central Asia—usually developed on windblown deposits, along piedmont areas, and on alluvial fans where rivers emerge from the mountains—are often highly productive when properly irrigated and fertilized. These soils sometimes are low in nitrogen and humus and accumulate excessive salts after prolonged cultivation. They require careful drainage and salinity control.

Other agriculturally useful soils include scattered pockets of productive alluvium on flood plains and some mountain soils in the

foothills of the Caucasus and Central Asia where terraced vineyards, pastures, and orchards have been established. Limited areas of red and yellow humid subtropical soils along the Black and Caspian Seas are important for growing tea, tobacco, rice, and citrus fruits.

Podzols and other agriculturally insignificant soils cover almost 70 percent of the territory of the USSR. Much of this same area is covered by permafrost. Podzols are poor, leached, and highly acid, having little agricultural value unless enriched by massive doses of fertilizer and lime. Even then only a small percentage can be significantly improved.

Soil group	Characteristics	Agricultural use
Chernozem	Fertility highest in USSR; drainage usually excellent; subject to wind and water erosion; some podzolization.	Wheat, corn, barley, sunflowers, sugar beets
Chestnut	Fertility second only to chernozem; highly subject to wind erosion; saline in some areas.	Spring wheat, barley, livestock
Gray & brown forest Turfy-podzolic	Fertility good to mediocre; drainage can be a problem in podzolic group; vulnerable to overcropping; need careful management and crop rotation.	Rye, oats, dairying, flax, market gardening, potatoes
Sierozem	Fertility very good to fair; occasionally deficient in mineral and organic nutrients; salinity often a problem; irrigation usually necessary.	Cotton, fruits, vegetables
Alluvial	Fertility extremely variable; flooding hazard.	Grazing and fodder crops on river bottoms, root crops and orchards on upper terraces
Mountain	Fertility highly diverse; subject to erosion; conservation measures needed.	Terraced vineyards and orchards
Podzolic	Fertility mediocre to very poor; drainage often very poor; needs fertilizers, liming for acidity, and artificial drainage.	Root crops, dairying, rye, hay

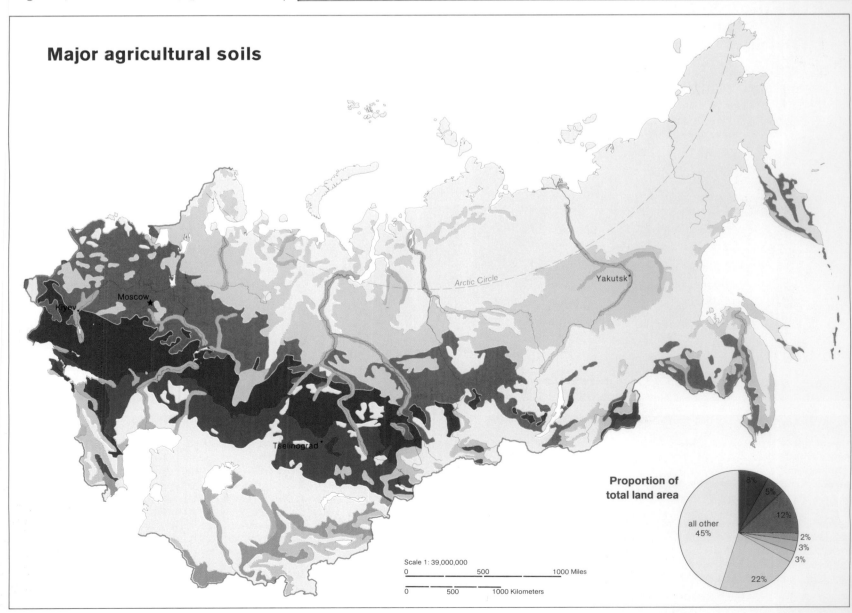

Major agricultural soils

Scale 1 : 39,000,000

0   500   1000 Miles

0   500   1000 Kilometers

Proportion of total land area

all other 45%

8%
5%
12%
2%
3%
3%
22%

Agricultural Land

Changes since 1950

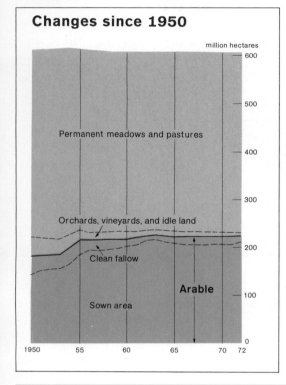

Approximately 27 percent of the total land area of the USSR is agricultural, and slightly more than one-third of the agricultural land is arable. The remainder of the agricultural land is in meadow, pasture, orchard, vineyard, or is idle.

In 1972, of the 224 million hectares of arable land in the USSR, almost all was sown. By comparison, U.S. arable land totaled 186 million hectares, of which less than three-quarters was sown. The USSR thus has more land under cultivation than the United States; however, Soviet land is less productive because of environmental disadvantages.

Since 1950, arable land in the USSR has been expanded by almost 43 million hectares, an area the size of California. The largest gain—29 million hectares—came during the New Lands program of 1953-58 when the dry, marginal areas of southern Siberia and northern Kazakhstan were brought under cultivation. During the 1960-63 period, the sown area was increased by 15 million hectares, to a record 218.5 million, primarily to

support the expanding livestock industry. Depletion of soil moisture subsequently forced the return of several million hectares to fallow. Continued pressure for increased production has led to the cultivation of meadows, pastures, idle land, abandoned farmstead and village land, and transportation rights-of-way.

It will be difficult for the USSR to expand further its arable land. Most land that will support sustained agricultural exploitation is already under the plow. Furthermore, gains already made through extension into marginal lands are continually being reduced by wind and water erosion and by salinization. Sizable losses of arable land (1.5 to 2 million hectares per year) result from urbanization and the establishment and growth of industrial sites, mining operations, and reservoirs. Future net growth in agricultural land will require extensive, well-planned, and expensive irrigation and drainage programs to develop potentially productive areas.

Distribution in 1970

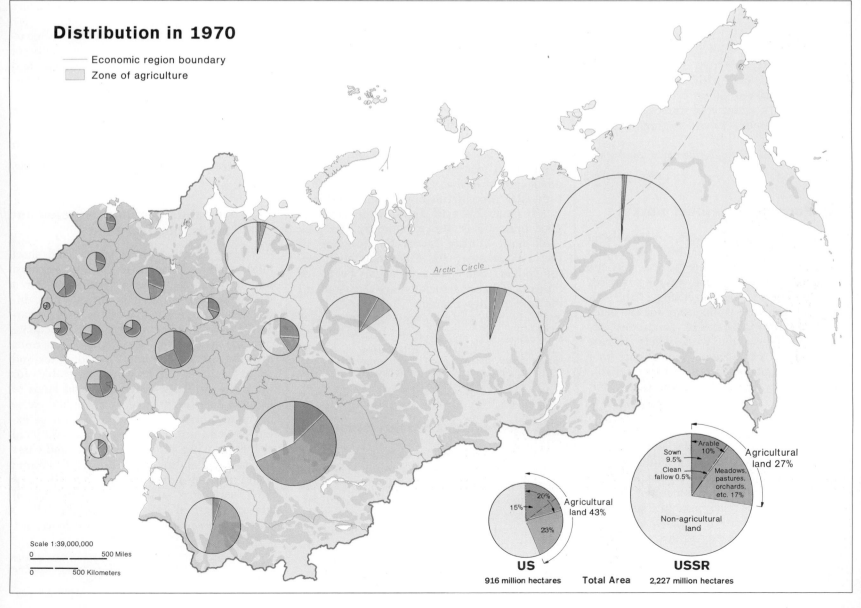

Economic region boundary
Zone of agriculture

Agroclimatic Regions

In so vast a country as the USSR, land use and crop mix vary substantially from one area to another, reflecting many factors—physical, cultural, and economic. But the controlling framework within which all of these factors operate is that of climate. The difference between the northernmost and the southernmost of the USSR's five broad agroclimatic regions is as great as the difference between Alaska and Southern California.

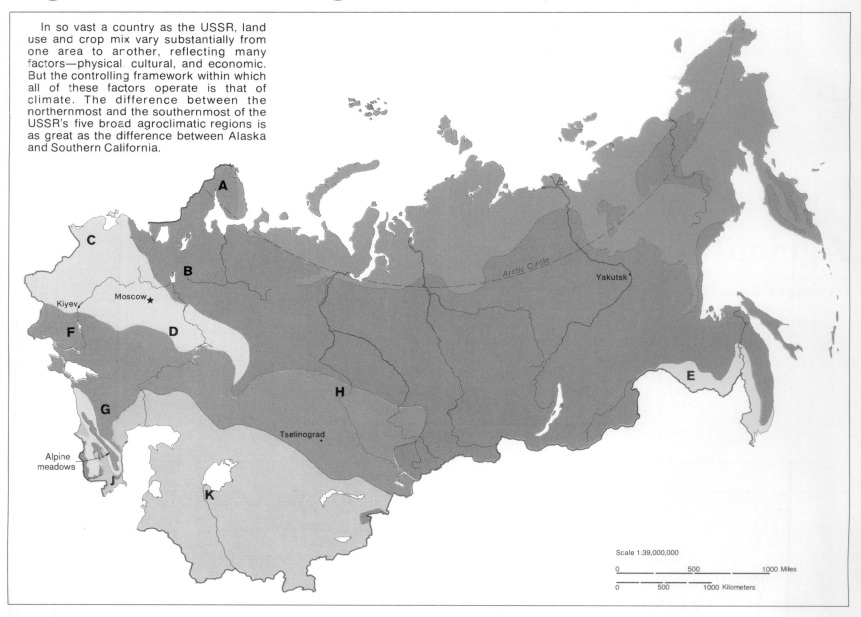

Scale 1:39,000,000

▨ Arctic agriculture

The cold, short summer severely limits agriculture in the almost uninhabited Arctic and sub-Arctic. Midsummer temperatures barely attain averages of 12°C, and the growing season lasts only two or three months. Little can be done with field crops, but greens and root vegetables can be grown on protected plots, under cold frames, or in hothouses. The tundra provides grazing lands for reindeer.

North American analogs: Northernmost Alaska and Canada.
Crop/Livestock: Greens, root vegetables, reindeer.

▨ Farming for a local market

Agriculture becomes more practicable in the vast forested region south of the tundra. Hardy, early-ripening crops grow despite the hazards of a short, cool growing season, severe winter, and deep freezing of the soil. Long summer days compensate for the short frost-free period. Growing conditions are most favorable in the west, where climate is moderated by the ocean. The soils are poor in nutrients but can produce fairly reliable harvests with draining, liming, heavy fertilizing, and growing of perennial grasses to help improve structure and nitrogen supply.

Farming is clustered around the typically small rural settlements and the few larger urban centers. The local agriculture helps ensure a dependable food supply for these remote settlements and reduces the volume of imports from the major agricultural regions to the south. The pattern of mixed farming is based on dairying, hardy grains, green fodder, and vegetables.

North American analogs: Central Alaska, much of Canada.

Crop calendars: A and B.
Crop/Livestock: Winter rye, oats, barley, potatoes, flax, hardy vegetables, hardy fruits, berries, reindeer, dairy/beef cattle, pigs, and attendant fodder crops.

▨ General farming

Though not the most important farming area in the USSR, this region makes a significant contribution to total agricultural output. Low summer temperatures reduce evaporation so that precipitation is generally sufficient and severe droughts uncommon. Winters are warmer in this region than in other extensive land areas at the same latitude. Soils are variants of podzolic and forest types, generally acid and low in fertility; poor drainage is also a handicap. But the cool moist climate favors the growing of rye and potatoes for food, oats and hay for fodder, and flax and sugar beets for industry. Closely associated are dairying and pig and poultry raising.

North American analogs: Area from Minnesota to New York.
Crop calendars: C, D, and E.
Crop/Livestock: Winter rye, oats, barley, buckwheat, spring wheat, potatoes, flax, hemp, sugar beets, soybeans in east, vegetables, fruits, dairy/beef cattle, pigs, and attendant fodder crops.

▨ Diversified, commercial farming

Fertile soils and milder climate make farming highly successful in this region. The soils, including the famous chernozem, are readily tilled and yield abundantly when given sufficient moisture. The treeless plains facilitate mechanized farming. Winters are mild; summers, warm to hot. The region's chief problem is the variability of rainfall. Unpredictable, severe droughts frequently result in crop failures, especially in the east and south. Irrigation and various measures for accumulating and conserving soil moisture assume great importance.

Despite the hazards, agriculture is characterized by intensity and by diversity of grain and industrial crops, livestock, and orchard products. This is the major wheat-producing region in the USSR.

North American analogs: Great Plains of the United States and Canada.
Crop calendars: F, G, and H.
Crop/Livestock: Winter wheat, corn, spring wheat and oats in east, sunflowers, sugar beets, potatoes, fruits, vegetables, grapes, dairy/beef cattle, sheep, pigs.

▨ Drylands grazing, irrigated and subtropical farming

A long, warm growing season and short mild winter characterize the southernmost region. Heat resources are sufficient for a wide range of crops; it is the moisture differences that produce variations in the character and intensity of farming. Adequate natural moisture in the Caucasus permits growing subtropical crops, including tea and citrus fruits, as well as winter vegetables for the north. In the semiarid and arid lands of Central Asia the grazing of sheep and cattle on natural pastures is the only form of extensive land use. However, desert soils yield rich crops when properly irrigated, and oases of irrigated farming concentrated around water sources produce many special crops such as cotton and rice. Dryfarming of grains is carried out near moist foothills.

North American analogs: Southern California, Arizona, and New Mexico.
Crop calendars: J and K.
Crop/Livestock: Cotton, corn, sorghum, rice, winter wheat, alfalfa, tea, tobacco, southern fruits including citrus, vegetables, grapes, sheep, cattle.

Regional crop calendars

Scale in centimeters

Dormancy

Intermittent snow cover | Average daily temperature above freezing | Sowing | Sprouting | Frost-free period | Ripening | Ripe | Average maximum depth of snow cover

| January | February | March | April | May | June | July | August | September | October | November | December |

A-Murmansk Oblast
115 cm (45.3 in.)

Winter rye
Oats
Potatoes
Cabbage
Berries

B-Vologda Oblast
56 cm (22.0 in.)

Winter rye
Spring wheat, oats
Barley
Potatoes
Flax

C-Lithuanian SSR
14 cm (5.5 in.)

Winter rye
Barley
Potatoes
Sugar beets
Flax

D-Mordva ASSR
34 cm (13.4 in.)

Winter rye
Spring wheat, oats
Buckwheat
Sugar beets
Hemp

E-Amur Oblast
16 cm (6.3 in.)

Spring wheat, oats
Barley
Buckwheat
Soybeans
Potatoes

F-Kirovograd Oblast
6 cm (2.4 in.)

Winter wheat
Barley
Corn
Sunflowers
Sugar beets

G-Stavropol' Kray

Winter wheat
Corn
Sunflowers
Orchards
Grapes

H-Omsk Oblast
37 cm (14.6 in.)

Spring wheat
Oats
Barley
Potatoes
Sunflowers

J-Azerbaijan SSR

Cotton
Winter wheat
Corn
Potatoes
Orchards
Grapes

K-Karakalpak ASSR

Cotton
Alfalfa
Corn
Sorghum
Rice
Orchards
Grapes

19

Part 2
Technology

A complex and diverse agricultural technology has been diffused, with difficulty, throughout the USSR. Irrigation canals cross the arid lands of Central Asia, drainage ditches dissect the wet Poles'ye, and vegetative windbreaks march hundreds of miles along the Volga. Experiments with modifying weather itself are under way. Fertility of poor soils has been improved through application of chemicals. Plant breeding to improve hardiness and yields is a major area of current research, as are efforts to cope with plant diseases and pests. Mechanical power has replaced human energy to a large extent in critical farm operations. A data base is being assembled for reappraisal of agricultural land use.

Notwithstanding these efforts, the level of agricultural technology in the USSR remains generally below that of other industrialized nations, a deficiency that coexists with a high level of scientific knowledge. Many Soviet agricultural scientists are world renowned, but the lag between research findings and their application continues to be unusually long in the USSR.

Soviet leaders have become increasingly aware of the need to modernize the USSR's farm sector and now place the highest priority on acquiring and assimilating the newest technology, especially in the areas of livestock breeding and feed grain production. The inventory of basic sowing and harvesting equipment is being steadily increased and the mechanization of livestock operations rapidly expanded through the introduction of large industrial-type feeding operations. The USSR has also sought to improve the production and application of agricultural chemicals through trade agreements and technical exchanges. The Soviet leadership wants especially to benefit from the expertise of the United States through technical exchanges and acquisition of U.S. methods and equipment. Exchange visits of US and USSR experts in integrated pest control and in plant genetics have been arranged. Joint study groups on problems of wind erosion in arid lands and on irrigation technology have benefited scientists of both countries.

In acquiring foreign technology, as well as in extending and constructing new land improvement projects, the amount of capital the leadership is willing and able to invest will be a critical factor. In addition, the effective diffusion of newly acquired technology will require basic changes in many of the attitudes, habits, and skills of Soviet farmers.

Fertilizer

Since the early 1960's the USSR has placed a high priority on increasing the supply of mineral fertilizers. The supply was quintupled between 1960 and 1973, and additional increases are programmed. The use of organic fertilizer—manure, compost, and peat—is also increasing. Enough liming materials, essential for effective fertilizer use and applied chiefly to the acid soils of the non-chernozem regions, are to be produced to cover 32 million hectares during the current five-year plan.

The quality of Soviet fertilizer, in terms of nutrient content, is relatively low—29.3 percent compared to the U.S. 40 percent in 1970. Only 5 percent of the Soviet production is made up of complex multinutrient fertilizers, compared with more than 50 percent for the United States. Actual nutrient available per unit of arable land in the USSR in 1972 was about 30 percent less than in the United States.

Soviet studies indicate that on the average each 100 kg (standard units) of mineral fertilizer applied will provide an additional yield per hectare of 100 to 200 kg for grain and 600 to 1,200 kg for sugar beets, potatoes, and vegetables. They also claim that each ruble spent in producing, transporting, and applying fertilizer will produce 2.5 to 3 rubles' worth of additional agricultural output. The USSR is relying on the increased use of fertilizer to provide nearly 40 percent of the gain in total gross farm output from 1971 to 1975.

In Central Asia, the Belorussian SSR, the Baltic Republics, and the northwest RSFSR, supplies of mineral fertilizer per unit of arable land have been much higher than the average for the country as a whole. Supplies were average or better in the naturally fertile black earth region of the Ukraine and very

low in the Urals, Siberia, and Kazakhstan. Industrial crops have traditionally been major recipients of fertilizer, but recent increases in fertilizer production have been allocated mainly to grain and fodder crops. Grain received 32 percent of supplies in 1970 and 35 percent in 1973.

The distribution of fertilizer is marked by excessive losses of up to 15 percent of shipments. The main causes are the poor physical and chemical qualities of mineral fertilizer—such as too much moisture, dusting, caking, and acidity—and the lack of proper packaging materials, transport containers, and loading equipment.

To cope with these problems the USSR is taking steps to increase production and to improve the quality of fertilizer. Agrochemists are attempting to perfect highly concentrated fertilizers in moisture-free granule form that can be efficiently transported and stored. Planned increases in the average nutrient content of fertilizer are also expected to lower costs of packaging, storage, and application. The USSR has recently concluded agreements with Japan and the United States to obtain facilities, materials, and technical expertise for producing more highly concentrated ammonia and triple superphosphate fertilizers.

There are also plans to provide greater numbers of properly equipped railroad cars, trucks, loading equipment, warehouses, and spreading machines. Expansion is planned in the network of agrochemical laboratories initiated in 1964 to provide technical advice and recommendations for more effective storage, preparation, and application of fertilizers. Even with good results from these programs, optimum fertilizer production and distribution will require sustained effort.

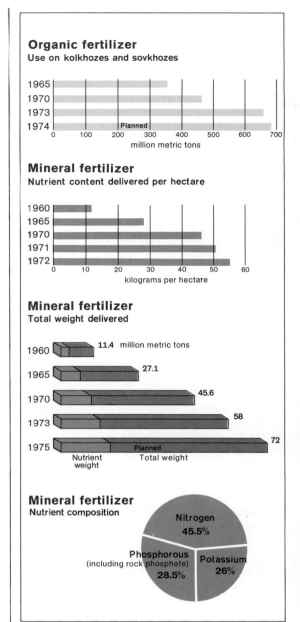

Organic fertilizer
Use on kolkhozes and sovkhozes

Mineral fertilizer
Nutrient content delivered per hectare

Mineral fertilizer
Total weight delivered

Mineral fertilizer
Nutrient composition

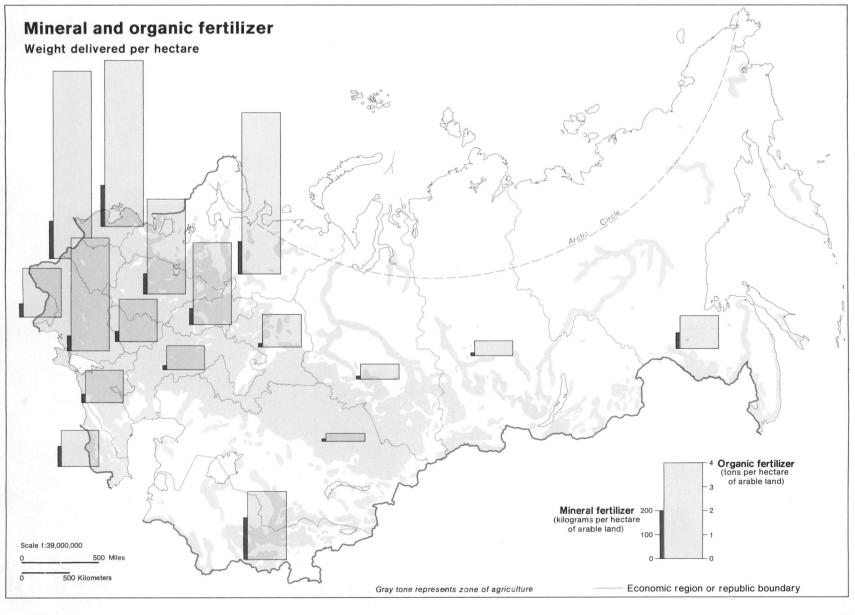

Mineral and organic fertilizer
Weight delivered per hectare

Scale 1:39,000,000

0 — 500 Miles

0 — 500 Kilometers

Gray tone represents zone of agriculture

Mineral fertilizer 200 (kilograms per hectare of arable land) 100 0

Organic fertilizer (tons per hectare of arable land)

Economic region or republic boundary

Irrigation and Drainage

The construction of irrigation and drainage systems is essential to the expansion and improvement of agriculturally productive land in the USSR. Although costly, these systems initially raise yields dramatically, and subsequently they stabilize production. The cost per hectare for a drainage system averages about 3,000 rubles and for an irrigation system, 5,000 to 6,000 rubles. The cost recovery period is claimed to be 3 to 4 years if the land is properly utilized, but in most instances it is probably longer.

In 1972, Soviet irrigated land totaled 12.0 million hectares (U.S. total, 16.5 million hectares). Drained land was 11.4 million hectares. Neither category constitutes a large proportion of all agricultural land, but each has a significant role in crop production. Irrigated land in particular is important for the production of specialty crops in Central Asia and the Transcaucasus.

The current Five-Year Plan (1971-75) calls for the development of 3.2 million irrigated hectares. This contrasts with the 1966-70 period, when irrigated land increased by only 1.2 million hectares. Progress to date indicates that the goal probably will be met. At the conclusion of the Plan, Soviet irrigated land is to total 13.7 million hectares. The largest amount of irrigated land—43 percent of the total—is located in Central Asia, where irrigation has for centuries played a major role. The most rapid expansion of irrigated land is in the drought-plagued, major grain-growing region of southeast European USSR. Expansion in the Far East has been small, but irrigation plays an important part in the development of areas along the border with China.

Furrow irrigation is the principal type practiced in the Soviet Union. Sprinkler irrigation—a more efficient means of utilizing water resources—is being introduced at a rapid rate in the Ukraine, Lower Volga, and North Caucasus. It is presently used on about 8 percent of the irrigated area, compared to 25 percent in the United States. Systems in use include the tractor-boom, tractor-spout, center-pivot, and wheel. The center-pivot system, which covers a circular area with a radius up to 456 m (1,500 ft), is favored. The Soviet "Fregat" is comparable to the U.S. "Valley" model used in the Columbia River reclamation project. Flood irrigation is limited to the flood plains of watercourses, and it is usually a one-time watering operation.

Covered conduits and lined canals are being installed in the USSR to counter water losses through evaporation and seepage. Canal liners—such as polyethylene—and protective films to retard surface evaporation are also in use or in various stages of experimentation. In some areas underground drainage networks are being installed together with irrigation systems to facilitate the washing of saline soils. Automation of water supply, distribution, and removal facilities is being undertaken in conjunction with the development of new or renovated systems.

The net increase in drained land during the current Five-Year Plan is expected to be about 3 million hectares—larger than additions recorded in previous five-year plans. Despite an apparent reduction shown in the Soviet statistics for 1967 (2.4 million hectares), there has been a steady increase in drained land since 1960. The drop shown for 1967 is probably the result of a more exact land census.

Most of the Soviet drained land is located in western European USSR. In 1972, half of the 8.5 million hectares used for agriculture was in fodder and grain crops (primarily barley and wheat) and most of the remainder in pasture and hayland. The cultivated land produced grain with an average yield of 36 bushels per acre, substantially higher than the national average of 25 bushels per acre. Additional construction of drainage systems is called for in the reclamation program for the non-chernozem region recently announced by Secretary Brezhnev.

Despite extensive experience in draining wetlands, the USSR has developed drainage technology slowly. Machines in use generally are modifications of earlier models. Soviet plastic tile was developed elsewhere and is used on only a small scale. Automation of drainage operations is limited. Deficiencies in machine quality and in tile materials plague wetland reclamation projects. However, Soviet efforts to overcome these problems continue.

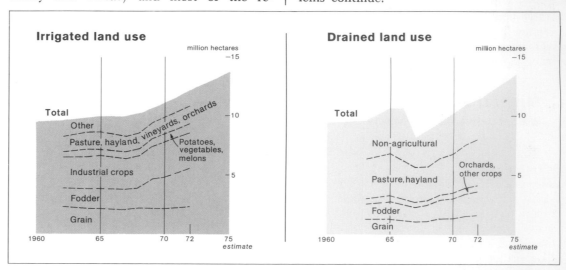

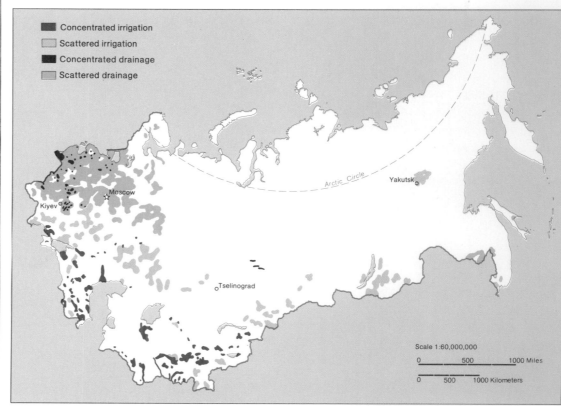

... in Southeast European USSR

Southeast European USSR, consisting of the North Caucasus and Volga Regions and parts of the Ukraine, is a major agricultural area that is frequently plagued by droughts and desiccating winds. The resultant wide fluctuations in yields have stimulated a concerted effort to extend irrigation throughout the area. The land under irrigation has already doubled since 1965, and the current Five-Year Plan (1971-75) calls for irrigated land to be increased by approximately 1.4 million hectares in the three regions included in the area.

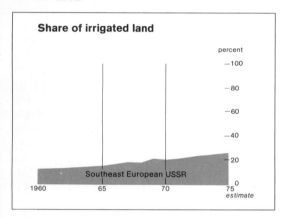

Share of irrigated land

Fodder crops are now planted on approximately half of the sown irrigated land in order to provide feed for local livestock and to enhance crop rotation. Grain crops are also important in the newly irrigated land. Fields planted to rice account for more than half of the country's rice production. Industrial crops (primarily sugar beets and sunflowers) occupy only a small part of the irrigated land—a pattern which contrasts sharply with land use in Central Asia, where industrial crops (primarily cotton) predominate.

The North Caucasus Region contains the largest concentration of irrigated land (1.3 million hectares) in this area, most of it along the lower Kuban' and Don Rivers and adjacent to the Terek and Kuma Rivers, which flow into the Caspian Sea. Projects now under way involve the expansion of existing irrigation systems along the lower Kuban' and Don Rivers and the development of the Velikiy Stavropol' system, which is an integral part of the long-term irrigation and water supply scheme for the central part of the Region. During the current Five-Year Plan, irrigated lands in the North Caucasus are to be augmented by 350,000 to 400,000 hectares, principally for the cultivation of rice and other grains.

Although there is presently relatively little irrigation in the Volga Region, long-term

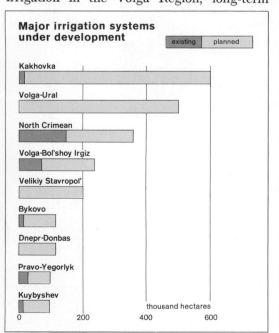

Major irrigation systems under development

plans are ambitious. According to a plan prepared by the Leningrad Institute of Water Management, about 8 million hectares would be irrigated for farming, of which 2 million would be developed in the 1976-80 period. Several projects for irrigating the fertile but arid lands east of the Volga River are already in an early stage of construction. The largest is the Volga-Ural system. When completed it will irrigate about 500,000 hectares for cultivation and provide enough water to an additional 2 million for grazing. This system also affects land use in the semidesert of western Kazakhstan. The recently completed Saratov Canal will permit further development of the Volga-Bol'shoy Irgiz system in the lands east of the Volga. However, if these and other systems are to be implemented successfully, a water supply in excess of the Volga's current capacity will be required. Completion of some projects undoubtedly will await construction of the Kama - Vychegda - Pechora river diversion scheme, which is to divert a substantial volume of water to the Volga River.

Forty percent of the planned 1971-75 increase in irrigated land in Southeast European USSR is in the Ukraine, where moisture conditions are somewhat better than in the eastern part of the area and returns on investment can be more quickly realized. Emphasis is being placed on the development of the two largest systems, Kakhovka and North Crimean; the trunk canal of the latter will supply water to Kerch', its terminus on the Crimean Peninsula.

Completion of a number of smaller irrigation projects (5,000-25,000 hectares) in Southeast European USSR will also make a substantial contribution to meeting the overall irrigation objectives.

The DDA-100M sprayer waters a 120-meter (400-foot) cultivated swath along a water supply ditch in the Rostov area

...in Soviet Central Asia

Agriculture in Soviet Central Asia is largely dependent on irrigation. Evaporation exceeds precipitation over most of the area, and without irrigation the fertile valleys and plains could support only a fraction of the present population and economic activity. Some of the highest mountains in the world rim Soviet Central Asia on the south; the snow and rain in these mountains feed the large rivers that flow into the lowlands, depositing alluvium and providing water for extensive canal networks.

Soviet Central Asia has approximately 5 million hectares of irrigated land. The main areas are situated along the Syrdar'ya and the Amudar'ya Rivers, which cross the deserts and empty into the Aral Sea. Other significant irrigated areas are supplied by several lesser streams—the Murgab, Tedzhen, Chu, and others—that flow northward out of the mountains and disappear into the sands.

Salinization of the soils because of poor drainage is a major problem in the irrigated areas. The soils are rich in alkalis, which are brought nearer to the surface when the water table rises. Until recent engineering improvements, more than half the soils in the Golodnaya Steppe irrigation project were affected by salinization problems. Soviet plans for new irrigation projects now call for drainage and irrigation canals to be constructed simultaneously.

The current Five-Year Plan (1971-75) calls for an increase in irrigated land in this region, with 650,000 hectares of the newly irrigated land in Soviet Central Asia and Transcaucasia to be planted in cotton. The primary focus is on the acceleration of projects in the Karshi Steppe (Kashka-dar'ya River), the Surkhandar'ya-Sherabad Steppe (Surkhandar'ya River), and the Fergana Valley (Syrdar'ya River). Work also continues on the large Golodnaya Steppe (Syrdar'ya River) project. Important projects such as the westward extension of the Karakum Canal to the Caspian, the Amu-Bukhara Canal (second phase), and the Great Namangan Canal will also bring water to the irrigable land. At completion, the Karakum Canal will be 1,450 kilometers long, the longest canal of any type in the world, nine times the length of the Suez.

Other efforts to maximize the use of the meager water supply of Soviet Central Asia include the development of *takyr* agriculture, a technique that uses accumulated water from the hard clay pans of the desert. Soviet researchers also are working on methods for melting glaciers in the mountains of this region, the use of mineralized ground water, artificial modification of weather, and the diversion of water from Siberian rivers.

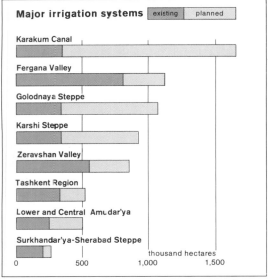

Major irrigation systems existing | planned

Karakum Canal

Fergana Valley

Golodnaya Steppe

Karshi Steppe

Zeravshan Valley

Tashkent Region

Lower and Central Amudar'ya

Surkhandar'ya-Sherabad Steppe

thousand hectares
0   500   1,000   1,500

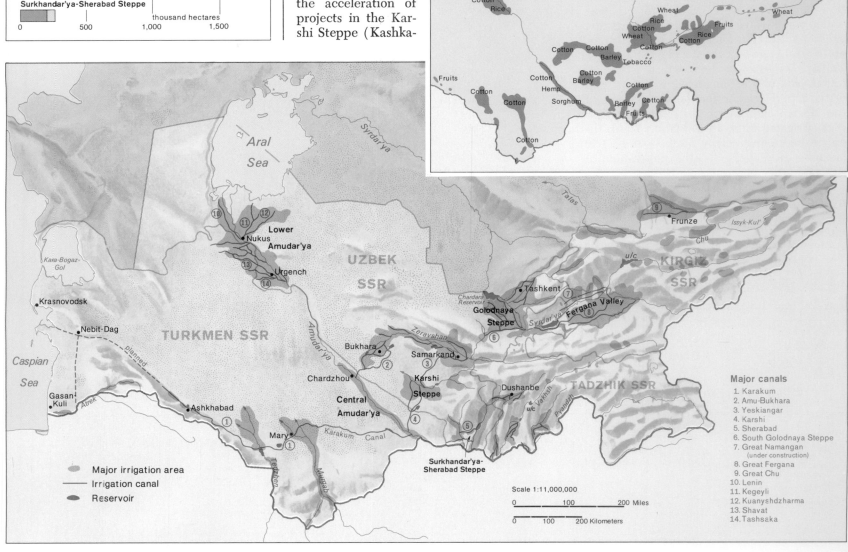

Major crops

Major irrigation area
Irrigation canal
Reservoir

Scale 1:11,000,000

0   100   200 Miles

0   100   200 Kilometers

Major canals
1. Karakum
2. Amu-Bukhara
3. Yeskiangar
4. Karshi
5. Sherabad
6. South Golodnaya Steppe
7. Great Namangan
   (under construction)
8. Great Fergana
9. Great Chu
10. Lenin
11. Kegeyli
12. Kuanyshdzharma
13. Shavat
14. Tashsaka

River Reversal

Continued expansion of irrigation in the southern regions of the USSR will require more water than is now available, and much potentially productive land will remain undeveloped unless new sources of supply can be tapped. Soviet water resource specialists predict that by 1985 almost all of the presently available resources of surface water along the lower Volga River and in major sectors of the basins of the Azov, Caspian, and Aral Seas will have been fully allocated. If present climatic and water-use trends continue, the annual water deficit in these basins could reach 130 km³ by 1985, resulting in further lowering of ground water tables and sea levels. Faced with a deficit of such magnitude, the Soviet Government is considering a number of proposals intended to provide these critical areas with additional fresh water.

The Kama-Vychegda-Pechora (KVP) reversal scheme, which dates from the mid-thirties, is designed to increase water supply in the Volga basin by diverting the upper courses of rivers that flow into the Arctic Ocean. In its most recent (1969) form, the project, which is to be completed in three stages, would annually divert southward an estimated 36 km³ of water from the Pechora and Vychegda Rivers by way of the Kolva and the Kama. Like previous versions of the plan, however, this one necessitates the flooding of what many Soviet authorities consider to be excessively large tracts of land valued for its timber and mineral potential.

The diversion of a number of other streams and lakes in the European North is also being studied. While the overall potential of these sources has not yet been established, it seems certain that they could make a substantial contribution to the relief of arid areas in the Caspian and Azov basins. Should they be tapped in conjunction with a completed KVP project, water supply problems in Volga-served areas would probably be alleviated for many decades.

Proposals have also been advanced for the diversion of northward flowing streams in West Siberia. Currently under examination is the Ob'-Irtysh-Tobol scheme, which calls for the construction of a dam and reservoir near Tobol'sk, at the junction of the Tobol and Irtysh Rivers. Water would be pumped from the reservoir and raised to an elevation of 75 to 80 meters near Zavodoukovsk, permitting it to flow by gravity to areas of irrigated agriculture adjacent to the Aral and Caspian Seas. The completion of the Ob'-Irtysh Canal, now under construction, will not only increase the water supply in the Irtysh but also will permit irrigation in areas along the canal itself.

Soviet sources indicate that the Ob'-Irtysh-Tobol plan could supply Central Asia with some 50 km³ of water annually at an intermediate stage of construction, and more subsequently. Upon completion—within 30 to 50 years—they claim it will be possible to irrigate a total of 34 million hectares of land in Central Asia and Kazakhstan, where now only about 6.4 million hectares are irrigated. The diversion would also benefit West Siberia, where 40 to 50 million hectares of wasteland could possibly be drained and brought into cultivation.

The KVP and the Ob'-Irtysh-Tobol schemes appear to be well within existing Soviet technical capabilities, and the need to get more water into the south relatively soon is evident. The capital requirements, however, are large, judging from the amount of earthwork involved in the construction of planned canals and dams. Although nuclear excavation has been proposed as an alternative to conventional techniques, the use of even the minimal amount of earth-moving equipment and other vehicles required for these projects could hamper construction elsewhere in the country. This consideration, in addition to the inevitable environmental disruption, may continue to delay all-out action on these massive projects.

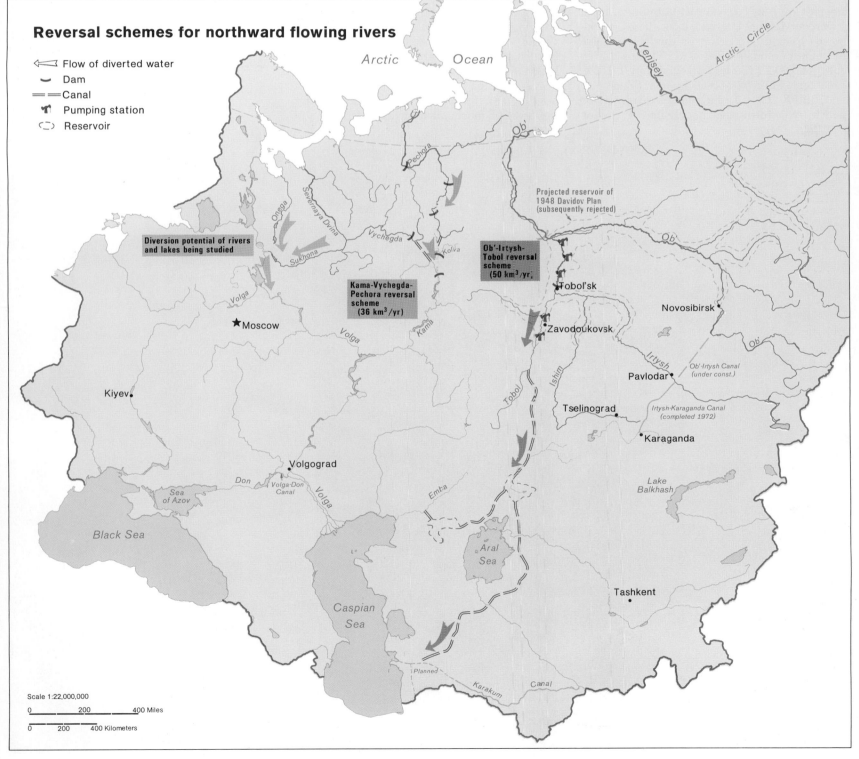

Reversal schemes for northward flowing rivers

- Flow of diverted water
- Dam
- Canal
- Pumping station
- Reservoir

Diversion potential of rivers and lakes being studied

Kama-Vychegda-Pechora reversal scheme (36 km³/yr)

Ob'-Irtysh-Tobol reversal scheme (50 km³/yr)

Projected reservoir of 1948 Davidov Plan (subsequently rejected)

Ob'-Irtysh Canal (under const.)

Irtysh-Karaganda Canal (completed 1972)

Arctic Ocean
Arctic Circle
Yenisey
Ob'
Pechora
Onega
Severnaya Dvina
Vychegda
Sukhona
Kolva
Volga
Kama
Moscow
Tobol'sk
Novosibirsk
Zavodoukovsk
Pavlodar
Irtysh
Ishim
Tobol
Kiyev
Tselinograd
Karaganda
Lake Balkhash
Volgograd
Volga-Don Canal
Don
Emba
Sea of Azov
Black Sea
Aral Sea
Caspian Sea
Tashkent
Planned
Karakum Canal

Scale 1:22,000,000

0   200   400 Miles

0   200   400 Kilometers

Mechanization

Agriculture in the USSR is less mechanized than in the United States, but the amount and overall quality of machinery and the horsepower available per hectare of cropland have increased steadily in the past decade. The USSR now has almost half as many tractors and trucks in agriculture as does the United States, as opposed to 1960, when it had only one-fourth as many. Further modernization of the USSR's farm sector will require increasing the inventory of basic farm machinery and assimilating new technology. New tractors and grain combines are continually being added, and mechanized equipment for planting and harvesting non-grain crops and for other agricultural operations is being developed or improved. In particular, mechanization is vitally important to the success of numerous large industrial-type livestock complexes currently under construction.

Soviet planners estimate that 3 to 4 million tractors are needed in agriculture; only 2 million are now in service. The most important tractors in numbers and utility are the tracked T-74, DT-75, and newer DT-75M (90 hp) and several models of the wheeled MTZ-50. About 40 percent of all Soviet tractors are tracked, contrasted to only about 5 percent in the United States. The "work-horse" tractors are being gradually replaced by newer models—T-150 (150 hp), DT-75M, and T-4 (130 hp) tracked and T-150K (165 hp), MTZ-52 (55-60 hp), MTZ-80 (80 hp), and K-700 (215 hp) wheeled tractors—which will form the backbone of Soviet

agriculture in the near future. These new models compare favorably with U.S. counterparts in horsepower, drawing power, and fuel consumption; the MTZ-80, for example, has been tested by the University of Nebraska with good results. Soviet agriculturists claim, in addition, that the new grain combines—Niva, Kolos, and Sibiryak—have a harvesting capability comparable to U.S. models. The USSR has almost as many combines as the United States, but fewer are available per hectare of grain cropland, a considerable impediment to harvesting grain at the optimum time.

Soviet farm equipment has a short life span; generally, Soviet tractors last about half as long as those in the United States because of lower quality, more intensive use, and poorer maintenance and repair. Spare parts are high priced, in short supply, and often of poor quality. Longevity may increase as numbers increase, but there will still be a tractor shortage in 1975 even if the planned goal of 2.5 million is met.

Now that grain planting and harvesting are almost completely mechanized in the USSR, mechanization is being extended to other agricultural operations. There is still a need for grain drying equipment, less than one-fourth of the potato crop is harvested by combine, and only about one-third of the cotton crop is picked mechanically. Specialized machines such as carrot harvesters, tea pickers, and grape pickers have been used at least experimentally, but the level of mechanization in vegetable and

fruit growing remains low. On the other hand, harvesting sugar beets and mature ear corn is about 80 percent mechanized and scheduled to reach 90 percent by 1975. The production of equipment for harvesting fodder crops has recently been boosted to match the demands for increased livestock production.

Mechanization for achieving increased output of livestock products is emphasized in the current Five-Year Plan. Large integrated livestock complexes under development have mechanized systems for water supply; for processing, storage, and automatic dispensing of feed; and for removal and processing of manure for fertilizer. The objective is to increase labor productivity, lower production costs, and substantially increase average weight gains. Several of the 1,170 planned complexes have been completed near Moscow, Leningrad, and Kiyev; the largest provide indoor facilities for 30,000 head of cattle or 108,000 swine. These are much larger than similar installations in the United States, where open-air feedlots are more prevalent. More than 500 large poultry complexes are also planned, some with as many as 500,000 chickens, roughly comparable to the largest in the United States. Each complex will place new demands on Soviet agricultural management and technical expertise, and a difficult period of assimilating this new technology lies ahead.

Kolos combines harvesting barley in the Kuban'

Mechanization of crop operations
(kolkhoz & sovkhoz)

• 1965   • 1968   —— 1971

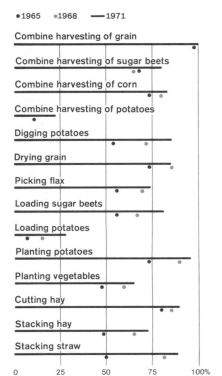

Combine harvesting of grain
Combine harvesting of sugar beets
Combine harvesting of corn
Combine harvesting of potatoes
Digging potatoes
Drying grain
Picking flax
Loading sugar beets
Loading potatoes
Planting potatoes
Planting vegetables
Cutting hay
Stacking hay
Stacking straw

0   25   50   75   100%

Mechanization of livestock operations
(kolkhoz & sovkhoz)

• 1965   • 1968   —— 1971   • 1975 (goal)

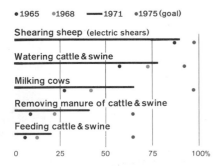

Shearing sheep (electric shears)
Watering cattle & swine
Milking cows
Removing manure of cattle & swine
Feeding cattle & swine

0   25   50   75   100%

Production and delivery of basic farm equipment

Tractors
thousands
500
400
300
200
100
0

Grain combines
100
50
0

Trucks
600
500
400
300
200
100
0

1960   65   70   72

▢ Total production
▢ Delivery to agriculture

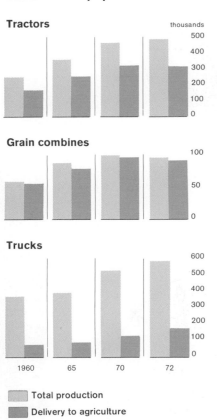

Inventory of basic farm equipment

	USSR				US
	1960	1965	1970	1972	1972
Number of tractors (thousands)	1,122	1,613	1,977	2,112	4,387
Total horsepower (millions)	47.6	77.6	111.6	124.3	212.0
Hectares of cropland for one tractor	196	138	113	107	30
Horsepower per 100 hectares of cropland	22	35	50	55	158
Number of grain combines (thousands)	497	520	623	656	703
Hectares of grain cropland for one combine	222	240	186	174	68
Number of trucks (thousands)	759	945	1,136	1,232	2,915

Belarus' MTZ-52 four-wheel-drive tractor with sugar beet combine

Belarus' MTZ-80 on test at the University of Nebraska

Belarus' MTZ-50, workhorse of agricultural operations

DT-75M, most numerous (48,900) tractor model delivered to agriculture in 1972

Land Use

The broad regional pattern of agricultural land use in the USSR reflects the environmental requirements of the basic crops. Each crop tends to be concentrated where the combination of heat, moisture, and fertility produces the best yields, although economic factors frequently cause displacement of the most environmentally suitable crop with one in greater demand. As elsewhere in the world, the agricultural land near urban areas and in densely populated industrial regions tends to be cultivated more intensively for high-value, perishable food crops. Selection of crops for use on very limited land resources also becomes an important factor in land-use patterns in the southernmost zone of the country, where environmental conditions favor cultivation of food and specialty crops.

Most of the cultivated fields in the USSR are planted in grains and fodder crops. The grains, primarily wheat and barley, cover more than half the cultivated area—winter wheat in the relatively mild area west of the Volga; spring wheat to the east, where the climate is too severe for winter crops; and barley, as a feed grain, throughout the agricultural belt. In the Ukraine and other fertile areas in the southwest, corn also is an important grain crop. Fodder crops—annual and perennial grasses and corn for silage and green feed—occupy about a third of the cultivated land. Much of the corn planted in northern regions does not mature in the short growing season and is cut green for livestock feed.

The Ukraine and the Central Chernozem Region have the superior soil necessary for sugar beets. Sunflowers, a major Soviet crop, require warmth but are drought resistant and therefore are cultivated extensively in the steppes of the Ukraine and the North Caucasus. Because of its short growing season, flax can tolerate the severe climate along the northern fringe of the agricultural zone. Potatoes, a staple Russian food, are well suited to the cool moist climate of central European USSR, the northern Ukraine, and Belorussia.

Only in the southernmost part of the USSR is the climate conducive to the growth of such valuable but fragile crops as cotton, tea, and citrus. In the irrigated fields of Soviet Central Asia, grain has been replaced by the more highly valued cotton, and in Moldavia and the Transcaucasus, orchards and vineyards also have been expanded at the expense of grain. Along the Black Sea coast the hilly terrain and mild climate are ideally suited for tea plantations, orchards, and vineyards.

Yield improvements have made it possible to meet increased demands for certain crops without further increases in acreage. The wheat area in Kazakhstan and West Siberia, for example, has declined since 1960, but higher yields have increased total production. Similarly, the area planted to cotton in Soviet Central Asia and the Transcaucasus has not expanded significantly in recent years, but the yields are much greater.

Major changes in land use in the USSR have been determined as much by the transient notions of Soviet leaders as by altered demand or yield improvements. The leaders' directives, translated into government procurement goals, are the most important factor in allocating land for planting.

Under Stalin's rule, the so-called *travopol'ye* grass rotation system of V. R. Vil'yams (Williams), an agrobiologist of American parentage, was adopted throughout the country without regard for local conditions. Perennial grasses were planted extensively in rotation with other crops to improve soil structure and add nutrients. The Vil'yams system was discarded by Khrushchev, who perceived extensive grass planting as a waste of arable land which could be devoted to grain crops.

Khrushchev, convinced of the value of corn as livestock feed, advocated corn planting on a vast scale in the middle and late 1950's, especially in the fertile western regions. Corn hectarage increased about eight times from 1953 to 1960. Wheat was pushed eastward to the virgin and long-fallow lands of northern Kazakhstan and West Siberia. After severe droughts in the early 1960's and Khrushchev's departure, the area sown to corn shrank and wheat hectarage increased. By 1970, total corn

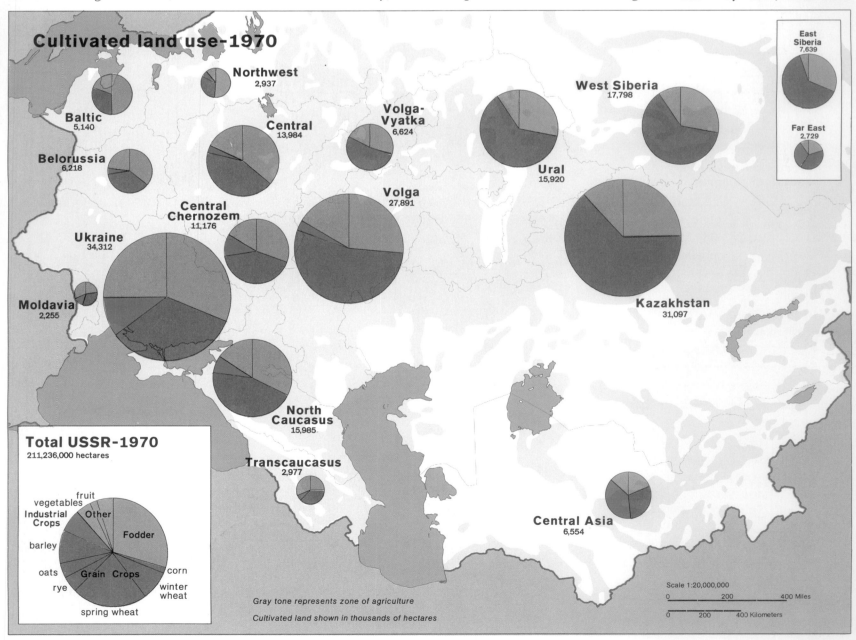

Cultivated land use-1970

East Siberia 7,639

Northwest 2,937

West Siberia 17,798

Baltic 5,140

Central 13,984

Volga-Vyatka 6,624

Far East 2,729

Belorussia 6,218

Ural 15,920

Central Chernozem 11,176

Volga 27,891

Ukraine 34,312

Kazakhstan 31,097

Moldavia 2,255

North Caucasus 15,985

Transcaucasus 2,977

Central Asia 6,554

Total USSR-1970
211,236,000 hectares

fruit
vegetables
Industrial Crops
Other
barley
Fodder
oats
Grain Crops
corn
rye
winter wheat
spring wheat

Gray tone represents zone of agriculture

Cultivated land shown in thousands of hectares

Scale 1:20,000,000

0   200   400 Miles

0   200   400 Kilometers

planting was only three-quarters of the 1960 figure. The shift was most dramatic in the North Caucasus but significant also in the Ukraine, Belorussia, and the Central Chernozem Region.

Khrushchev believed that fallowing was a wasteful use of arable land and forced its reduction. Yields decreased. After he was replaced, increased fallowing again became an integral part of the rotation pattern. Fallowing today is used extensively to control moisture losses and weeds and to build up nutrients in the soil. The choice between clean fallow, where the fields are plowed, and stubble fallow (or stubble mulching) has been hotly debated. As the use of fertilizers increases, however, the importance of fallowing and grasses in rotation schemes may diminish.

The Brezhnev regime has not been associated with such single-crop agricultural campaigns as Stalin's grasses or Khrushchev's corn. Although grain production has been a continuing preoccupation, the approach has been pragmatic and environmental limitations have been taken into account. The recently announced plan to intensify agricultural land use and reclaim presently unused areas in the non-chernozem regions of the RSFSR, where moisture is generally adequate, should permit an expansion of fodder crops. That, in turn, could permit some land in other parts of the country to be diverted from fodder to feed grains.

Efforts to bring more and more land into agricultural use in the USSR have generally obscured the need to promote the best, most intensive use of land already devoted to agriculture. The underlying assumption that land resources are unlimited and awaiting "mastery" has dominated official programs; it has been replaced only slowly by the realization that each hectare must be put to its most productive use and developed in the optimal way.

A potentially important, but so far relatively ineffective, device to foster rational land use over the country as a whole is the regional system of government procurement prices. Under this system farms in regions with favorable natural conditions receive lower prices for a given product than farms in less favored regions. The objective is to maximize total production by making farming in southern Siberia, for example, as "profitable" as farming in the Ukraine. The system is also a means of controlling land use and promoting regional specialization. The established price regions, however, are generally too large and are based on administrative units rather than on natural regions. To correct this situation and to aid land use planning, a detailed land survey was initiated in 1968. The results of this survey should provide a better basis for future land use and pricing programs.

Soviet agriculturists refer to a "field system," such as a nine-field rotation or a five-field rotation, rather than to the number of different crops through which a given field passes, as in the United States. A work brigade is charged with implementing the system in a way that maintains the land in good condition and at the same time meets production quotas.

In Soviet Central Asia, with irrigation, the rotational pattern is 3 or 4 years of alfalfa, then 4 or 5 years of cotton. When grasses are part of the rotation system, an additional benefit is derived.

In western regions, where both winter and spring crops can be sown, a rotational pattern may be a nine-field crop rotation. Over a 9-year period, each field is planted once to each crop.

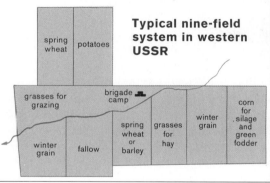

Typical nine-field system in western USSR

spring wheat | potatoes

grasses for grazing | brigade camp | | corn for silage and green fodder

winter grain | fallow | spring wheat or barley | grasses for hay | winter grain

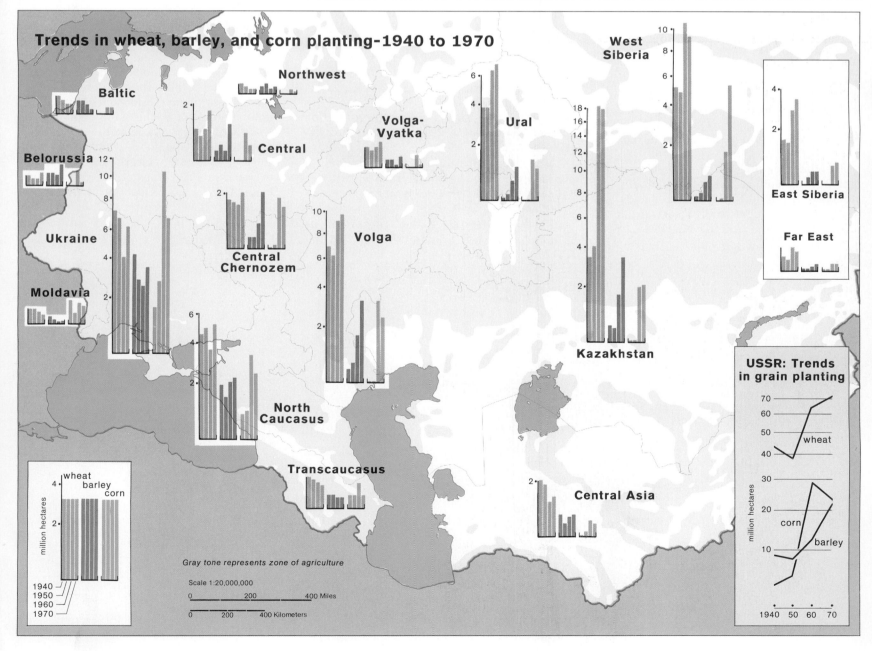

Trends in wheat, barley, and corn planting—1940 to 1970

Baltic
Northwest
Belorussia
Ukraine
Moldavia
Central
Central Chernozem
Volga-Vyatka
Volga
North Caucasus
Transcaucasus
Ural
West Siberia
East Siberia
Far East
Kazakhstan
Central Asia

Gray tone represents zone of agriculture

Scale 1:20,000,000

0 — 200 — 400 Miles
0 — 200 — 400 Kilometers

wheat
barley
corn

million hectares

1940
1950
1960
1970

USSR: Trends in grain planting

million hectares

70
60
50
40
30
20
10

wheat
corn
barley

1940 50 60 70

Erosion Control

Soviet farmland is subject to severe wind and water erosion, and in many areas these natural processes have been accelerated by traditional farming practices that were geared to exploitation of the land rather than to its conservation. Plowing of steep slopes, overgrazing, and other practices that exhaust the soil and remove vegetative cover have been particularly damaging in the forest-steppe and forest zones of the European USSR and in the Transcaucasus. In the dry steppe and semidesert, bare ground is exposed frequently to strong, dry winds, which remove the top layers of the soil, scattering it in the form of fine dust. It has been estimated that .5 to 1.5 million hectares of cropland are completely removed from cultivation each year by wind erosion and that an area many times that large is damaged to some degree.

Dust storms are actually becoming more frequent because soil stripped of vegetative cover can be dislodged by winds of lower velocity than before. In the grain-growing Kuban' and southern Volga regions, for example, dust storms occurred in 1960, 1964, and 1965; and in the winter of 1969 a storm completely destroyed crops on 820,000 hectares and severely damaged crops on 634,000 hectares in only 5 days.

The presence of thick deposits of wind-blown soil (loess) leads to another problem. Loess is very susceptible to deep gullying even on gentle slopes. The occasional downpours of rain in summer produce vast networks of gullies and ravines, particularly throughout the large areas of the Ukraine where deep loess deposits underlie the topsoil.

Hundreds of millions of bushels of grain and several million tons of fodder are lost annually in the USSR because yields are reduced on eroded land. Soviet estimates

Windbreaks shelter tea plantings in the Transcaucasus

indicate that the elimination of erosion on arable land would result in an annual increase in the national income of 4.5 billion rubles.

The severity of the erosion problem was acknowledged in a 1967 joint resolution of the Communist Party and the Council of Ministers. The resolution called for increased use of contour plowing, crop rotation, strip cropping, and sowing grass on steep slopes; planting and cultivating forest belts; afforestation of gullies, ravines, and shorelines of rivers and reservoirs; and the construction of erosion-control and flood-control installations.

Many Soviet organizations are involved in erosion control. The ministries of agriculture of the USSR and of its constituent republics play a major role, but not without occasional internal conflicts since these organizations also have a vested interest in maximizing current production. The USSR and republic ministries of land reclamation and water resources, the State Forestry Committee, research organizations, and ultimately the individual sovkhozes and kolkhozes all enter the picture.

Prominent among erosion control measures are windbreaks and shelterbelts, designed to combat both wind and water erosion. Concentrated on the steppe and forest-steppe of European USSR, these forest belts protect against wind erosion, increase the accumulation of snow, check the erosive action of surface waters, and raise the water table. In addition to the local windbreaks maintained by forestry farms, kolkhozes, and sovkhozes, a series of major shelterbelts, some 30 to 100 meters wide and hundreds of kilometers long, were established in the Volga-Don region as a result of a 1948 state decree. Altogether, about 2 million hec-

Gully erosion near Volgograd

LESLIE DIENES
Department of Geography

tares of land have been planted to wind-breaks and shelterbelts.

Contour plowing, crop rotation, fallowing, stubble-mulching, and terracing are soil-conservation practices long used in many areas; however, both crop rotation and fallowing have at times been controversial issues in the USSR since they withdraw land temporarily from production.

Stubble-mulch tillage is a necessity for adequate erosion control in the New Lands area of West Siberia and northern Kazakh-stan and in other moisture-deficient areas. Also called trashy fallow, this practice involves leaving crop residues and soil-improving crops at least partly on top of the ground instead of burning them or turning them under. Trashy fallow protects the soil from baking, contributes to lower soil temperatures in hot summer weather, decreases the degree of freezing, impedes runoff and evaporation and enables the soil to absorb more rainfall, and aids the growth of useful bacteria in the soil.

Various types of terraces are used in hilly terrain to reduce the gradient of the slope. Found primarily in the mountains of Moldavia, the Caucasus, and Soviet Central Asia, terracing was once considered the basis for mountain agriculture. Although research has shown that it is not indispensable on all slopes and for all crops, terracing is still practiced where control of surface runoff at the place of its formation is necessary.

The Soviet erosion control program has had some serious shortcomings. About two-thirds of the total area planted to shelter-belts before 1956 has been lost because of improper planning or subsequent neglect. Many shelterbelts even today are deteriorating through neglect, and others are failing because they were planted in regions too dry for adequate growth. Fallowing, especially in the New Lands, has often been overlooked—to the detriment of future soil productivity. Finally, while stubble-mulching in the USSR has expanded in the past several years to more than 20 million hectares, better equipment design and more machines are still needed.

Conservation of land through erosion control will take on added importance as capital outlay requirements increase for land recovery projects and opportunities decrease for expanding agricultural land into virgin areas.

Region	Environment	Erosion	Controls
Central Russian Upland	Hilly relief; depleted soils; occasional heavy, prolonged rains	Networks of *ovragi* (actively growing V-shaped gullies); sheet erosion	Runoff diversion canals and ditches; grasses and trees as stabilization plantings in gullies; fertilizers
Central & Southern Ukraine	Loess-based soils; summer downpours; occasional drought and *sukhovey*	Networks of *ovragi*; sheet erosion; dust storms	Diversion canals; trees and grasses in and around the *ovragi*; contour plowing; windbreaks
Kuban'	Light-textured soils; summer cloudbursts; frequent *sukhovey* and occasional drought	Rilling; sheet erosion; dust storms	Windbreaks; irrigation; fertilizers
Volga Upland	Steep slopes; soils underlain by sandstone, limestone and loess; occasional intense rains; frequent *sukhovey* and periodic drought	*Ovragi* topography; sheet erosion; severe dust storms; occasional flash floods	Long north-south shelterbelts; local windbreaks; terraces; diversion canals; contour plowing; trees and grasses planted in the *ovragi*
Transcaucasus	High local relief; rains and melting snow in spring; sparse vegetation	*Balki* (very old ravines and gullies); networks of *ovragi*; sheet washing; flash floods; mudslides	Terraces; local windbreaks; fertilizers
New Lands	Moisture-deficient area; dry, pulverized, light-textured soils; sparse vegetative cover; frequent *sukhovey* and drought	Wind-scouring topsoil deflation; severe dust storms	Windbreaks; strip cropping (summer fallow); stubble-mulch tillage
Central Asia	Light, sandy soils; aridity; desiccated soil; lack of vegetation; frequent *sukhovey*	Violent dust storms; shifting sand dunes; flash floods and landslides in the mountains	Windbreaks; saxaul trees and cover crops as stabilizing agents; irrigation

31

Pest Control

Soviet officials estimate the value of crops lost to pests—insects, rodents, plant pathogens, weeds, etc.—at 12 billion rubles annually. (Official statistics for 1972 valued harvested crops at 40 billion rubles.)

Pesticides are in short supply in the USSR despite increased production over the past decade. In 1970, the Soviet Union reportedly met its needs for insecticides and fungicides by only 60 percent and its requirements for weed killers by only 50 percent. Prospects are poor through the 1970's for filling this gap between supply and demand. To help alleviate the shortage, the USSR has included pesticides among the industries being developed and upgraded under the aegis of the Council for Mutual Economic Assistance, which regulates Soviet-East European economic cooperation.

Early Soviet dependence on chloro-organic compounds has been reduced in favor of the more effective phosphoro-organic and carbamate compounds. For these, the USSR relies primarily on compounds originally developed in the United States, Europe, and Japan, since its own research and development is less advanced.

Less pesticide per hectare is used in the USSR than in the United States because the USSR has less pesticide available for a larger area of cropland. This situation plus a shortage of pesticide application equipment means that some crops go untreated or do not get the benefit of multiple treatment. Resort to manual labor—hand weeding, for example—only partially counterbalances these deficiencies.

Both the Soviet Union and the United States rely heavily on aerial application of pesticides. The United States applies a higher percentage from the air, but more total area is treated this way in the USSR. In 1972, 39 percent of all Soviet pesticides were applied from aircraft. This method plays a particularly important role in the application of weed killers (59 percent in 1970) and defoliants applied to cotton prior to mechanical harvesting (100 percent in 1970).

Soviet concern over the ecological impact of chemical pesticides has led to a reduction in the import and production of persistent chloro-organic and mercury compounds, strict regulation of highly toxic pesticides, and increased emphasis on non-chemical methods of plant protection. The Ministry of Health, which screens pesticides, has banned the importation and use of the more highly toxic compounds.

Environmental concern, chronic shortages of chemical pesticides, and the high cost of the escalating war on pests have also stimulated the Soviet Union to develop a program of integrated pest control. The program includes the coordinated use of chemical pesticides, improved cropping practices, pest-resistant crop varieties, and biological methods—insect predators, pest lures, and insect sterilization techniques. Although the Soviet Union has made significant advances, progress is hindered by insufficient skilled manpower, equipment, and coordination of research. For example, research laboratories in the field of biological controls are, despite a major effort, poorly equipped, understaffed, and without good quality control. The exchange of information and cooperation among agriculturists, academic researchers, and industry is inadequate.

The USSR claims that plant protection activities annually save more than 5 billion rubles worth of crops. This amount represents about 12 percent of the total value of all crops produced. Estimates of savings for the early 1960's were 2.6 billion rubles; the goal for 1975 is 8 billion rubles. The latter would seem a highly optimistic figure, since none of the indices of pest control technology is rising at a rate high enough to produce such an increase in effectiveness.

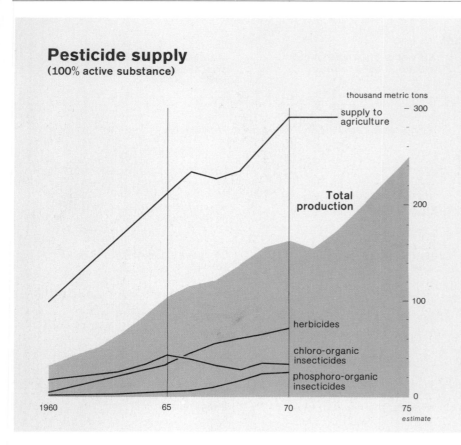

Pesticide supply
(100% active substance)

thousand metric tons

supply to agriculture

Total production

herbicides

chloro-organic insecticides

phosphoro-organic insecticides

1960   65   70   75
estimate

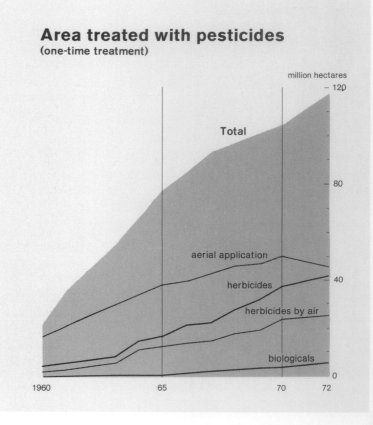

Area treated with pesticides
(one-time treatment)

million hectares

Total

aerial application

herbicides

herbicides by air

biologicals

1960   65   70   72

To some extent infestations by insects and plant pathogens are regional: each insect or pathogen can tolerate only a limited range of temperature and moisture conditions. Pest distribution is also affected by the intensity of planting of host crops, the distribution of intermediate host crops or weeds, and cultivation practices such as timing and depth of plowing, which can destroy insect larvae in the soil. Time of sowing can affect the coincidence between the most vulnerable stages of crops and the most active stages of insects and pathogens.

The Soviet wheat crop is beset by numerous pests. In the New Lands of West Siberia and northern Kazakhstan, where wheat is the dominant crop, it is particularly susceptible to the late wheat shoot fly, which may reduce yields by as much as 30 percent. This insect is most damaging in dry years, when less shoot growth occurs to offset the early damage to the main stem by larvae. The gray grain moth also causes great damage in the New Lands because of the coincidence of egg laying with wheat-ear formation. Thrips are also particularly damaging in this region.

The frit fly thrives in the relatively moist areas of the northern Ukraine and the Central Chernozem Region and in the forest-steppe and steppe zones of West Siberia. The northern USSR is too cold for it. The hessian fly inflicts its most severe damage in the Ukraine, where extended warm autumn weather and the practice of growing both spring and winter wheat encourage the pest. The wheat stem sawfly is primarily a problem in the Ukraine and the North Caucasus. Gout flies are found in many regions but are especially damaging to winter wheat in the relatively moist Northwest.

Grain beetles infest crops in the southern European USSR but are generally excluded from Siberia and northern Kazakhstan by the deep freezing of the soil, which kills the larvae. Shield bugs are widespread, but the most damaging, the Eurygaster, is found mostly in the Ukraine, North Caucasus, and middle and lower Volga regions. Click beetles are a pest especially in wetter areas of the forest-steppe, and thus are a threat to wheat in the European USSR and West Siberia.

The most serious fungus diseases of wheat in the USSR are the rusts. Moist, warm regions and irrigated areas are the most susceptible; the drier areas east of the Volga and in much of Kazakhstan are less afflicted. Yellow rust, however, is found in cooler (northern or elevated) regions. Rusts annually reduce the winter wheat harvest by about 5 percent and the spring wheat by about 3 percent. Wheat smut is widespread, but it causes most damage in the Volga region, the Urals, Siberia, and Kazakhstan. Bunt is found in all regions. Root rot, also widespread, causes most harm in dry regions, notably in the area east of the lower Volga, in Kazakhstan, and in West and East Siberia. Harvest losses in hard-hit areas may reach 50 percent from this fungus disease.

Major crop pests

Insects, Mites, and Nematodes	Crops	Diseases
Eurygaster shield bug (especially in wheat) frit fly gout fly hessian fly late wheat shoot fly wheat stem sawfly grain beetles chinch bug click beetle (fireworm) gray grain moth thrips aphids cutworms	Wheat, Barley, Oats, Rye	stem rust brown leaf rust yellow stripe rust smut common bunt (especially in winter wheat) root rot Fusarium wilt powdery mildew
European corn borer corn sawfly cutworms wireworms	Corn	rust smut root rot stem blight corn mosaic
aphids miners	Rice	rice blast (Piricularia)
cotton moth spider mites	Cotton	wilt (caused especially by Verticillum fungus)
beet weevil beet flies beet fleas aphids	Sugar Beets	black root leaf spot mildew
Colorado potato beetle cutworms aphids leaf beetles cabbage moth potato stem nematodes	Vegetables and Potatoes	Phytophthora Fusarium wilt of potatoes mosaic viruses
pea weevils pod borers beetles aphids	Legumes	pod spot leaf blight downy mildew Fusarium wilt rust
codling moth apple leaf roller apple tree ermine moth European apple sawfly leopard moth white moth/fall webworm mites aphids scale insects	Fruit	scab powdery mildew
leaf rollers spider mites grape erineum mite grape phylloxera (plant lice)	Grapes	powdery mildew
sunflower beetle banded sunflower moth	Sunflowers	rust white rot powdery mildew

AN-2 aircraft spraying vineyards

Plant and Livestock Breeding

Plant breeding

Since the mid-1950's, Soviet genetic programs have developed rapidly on the basis of a large inventory of crop germ plasm which includes U.S. and many other foreign varieties. Despite the legacy of the Lysenko era, during which both research and training suffered, Soviet geneticists have some noteworthy accomplishments to their credit, including the breeding of high-yield wheat and sunflower varieties.

The development of high-yield varieties of grain with drought and disease resistance and non-lodging characteristics is the major objective of Soviet plant breeders. Although foreign grain varieties have been introduced, many have not been successful. For example, some wheats that grow short and stiff-strawed in the United States have lodged badly or failed to outyield Soviet varieties under conditions in the USSR. Soviet researchers are investigating trigeneric (wheat, quack grass, and rye) grain hybrids for characteristics to breed into existing varieties. One specific task is to develop a winter wheat variety with a high degree of resistance to winterkill that would adapt itself to the harsh environmental conditions of Siberia.

Plant breeding is the overall responsibility of the USSR Ministry of Agriculture, but the actual research is carried out by the All-Union Institute of Plant Industry and a number of all-union scientific research institutes. Each of the latter is concerned with a particular crop and has selection and experimental stations for testing seeds and new crop varieties. An agricultural testing facility is located in every oblast, autonomous republic, and *kray*.

Bezostaya-1, a primary winter wheat variety, was developed at the Krasnodar Scientific Research Institute for Agriculture. Because of its excellent bread-baking characteristics, it is sought by domestic and even foreign millers.

The development of Rostovchanka, a variety of winter wheat, illustrates the complex and protracted processes that lead to the introduction of a new commercial crop variety. The crossbreeding (Skorospelka 36 x Mironovskaya 264) was conducted in 1961 at a selection station in Rostov Oblast, and the initial elite plant was selected in 1964. The new variety was tested in 1967 and 1968 for yield, disease-, pest-, and drought-resistance, and adaptation to the local conditions. From 1969 to 1972 it was tested by the State Commission for Varietal Testing at six stations. During the 1967-72 testing period, average yields when sown after clean fallow ranged from 5 to 18 bushels per acre greater than the yield of the standard variety sown in the region. On the basis of the tests, Rostovchanka was recommended for sowing in the Rostov area. The new variety was certified by the USSR Ministry of Agriculture, which then directed that the seed be introduced in sufficient quantity to all appropriate kolkhozes and sovkhozes. Rostovchanka was finally sown commercially on 73,000 hectares for the 1973 crop.

Livestock breeding

Soviet efforts in livestock breeding have increased productivity as well as environmental adaptability. Special breeding farms have been established which control artificial insemination of livestock for each region of the country. In 1970, 71 percent of the cows, 74 percent of the sheep, and 15 to 20 percent of the swine on sovkhozes and kolkhozes were bred artificially.

Soviet breeders have traditionally developed dual-purpose cattle, for meat as well as milk production. The best example, the Simmenthal, introduced from Switzerland and crossed with local breeds, is now widely distributed. The Red Steppe, developed from East Friesian cattle in the 18th century, is another important dairy-beef breed. The Simmenthal and Red Steppe breeds total more than half of all cattle on kolkhozes and sovkhozes. Other significant breeds include Black-mottled, East Friesian, Yaroslavl, Brown Latvian, and Kholmogar—all of which are best for milk—and dual-purpose Kostroma, Bestuzhev, Schwyz, and Alatau. Most of these breeds either originated in Central Europe or were developed from native stock crossed with Danish, Dutch, French, and other breeds to produce hardy animals for specific climatic regions.

Although these dairy and dual-purpose cattle have dominated the livestock picture in the past, meat breeds have received greater attention in recent years. They constituted about 4 percent of 1971 cattle totals and will increase to 16 percent by 1975. More than 50,000 Aberdeen Angus, Hereford, Shorthorn, Santa Gertrudis, and Galloway have been imported, most during the last 10

Kazakh Whitehead, leading meat breed, shows evidence of Hereford ancestry.

years. They have been maintained as purebred herds or crossed with the two main Soviet meat breeds, Kalmyk and Kazakh. The Kazakh Whitehead, which combines Hereford with Kalmyk and Kazakh stock, has become the most important and most widely distributed meat breed in the USSR. It is fast-maturing, hardy, and especially adaptable to marginal dry steppe and semidesert lands. As of 1969, there were 861,000 Kazakh Whiteheads in the Kazakh SSR alone. Fast-maturing breeds will probably account for an increasing percentage of the cattle raised in the industrial-type complexes currently being promoted.

Swine breeding has been dominated by the Large White breed, originally imported from England. Large Whites provide good pork, bacon, and lard. Some specialized meat breeds are now being further developed by crossing Large Whites with Danish and Estonian meat breeds. Sheep breeding has concentrated mostly on selective development of native breeds, with adaptability to various climate and terrain conditions as important as refinement of wool types. Soviet Merino breeds dominate the fine-wooled sheep (62 percent) and accounted for about 40 percent of all the sheep in the USSR in 1969. The Karakul is the most important and numerous of the coarse-wooled sheep. Emphasis continues on developing breeds for high quality wool, and only 15 percent are raised for meat.

Environmental Modification

In recent years Soviet researchers have developed methods of modifying the weather to protect crops from violent storm damage or to increase available moisture or heat. These methods are now of modest significance in overall food production, but they will play an increasingly important role in some geographic areas.

The protection of crops from hail—particularly destructive in the Caucasus, Moldavia, and parts of the Ukraine and southeastern Central Asia, where valuable specialty crops are grown—is the objective of one of the most active weather modification projects. Local meteorological institutes began intensive hail research programs in the 1950's, conducted numerous hail suppression experiments in the 1960's, and by 1972-73 had developed a program that provided hail protection for about 4 million hectares of farmland. A leading Soviet researcher estimates that hail suppression would be economically feasible for about 17 million hectares in the USSR.

The hail program is supported by the Ministry of Agriculture and carried out by institutes of the USSR Hydrometeorological Service and the republic academies of sciences. Under the program hail-producing clouds, detected by radar, are systematically seeded with artificial crystallization reagents delivered by rockets or artillery. The purpose is to eliminate the large supply of supercooled water so that hail cannot develop or is so fine that it melts before reaching the ground. Soviet hail-control specialists claim to have reduced hail damage in protected areas by about 70 percent. According to the director of the USSR Hydrometeorological Service, the benefit-to-cost ratio was roughly 5:1 in 1972-73.

Other weather modification activities relating to agriculture are still essentially in the research stage. These include precipitation augmentation and thunderstorm suppression.

Research on precipitation augmentation has been conducted mostly in the Ukraine at a special test area near Krivoy Rog. In recent years, experiments have been extended to other parts of the country, such as northern Kazakhstan, the Lake Sevan area of Armenia, and the mountains of Central Asia.

The experiments in the Ukraine, seeding with crushed dry ice from aircraft, have had better results in winter than in summer. Winter precipitation, including snow for the protection of winter crops, could be increased by an average of 30 to 35 percent. In summer, the seeding of cumulus clouds produced only about a 1 percent increase in precipitation. Members of the USSR Hydrometeorological Service have concluded that precipitation augmentation is not large enough to warrant the cost of large-scale cloud seeding operations. There is also uncertainty about the feasibility of available techniques in moisture-deficient regions. However, research and experimentation continue.

Experiments in thunderstorm suppression are aimed at reducing the damage, especially to orchards, caused by heavy rains and strong winds. Thunderstorms are dispersed by creating artificial downdrafts in the clouds. One method is to seed them with insoluble agents such as cement. Soviet investigators claim that about 95 percent of seeding attempts successfully slowed down or stopped

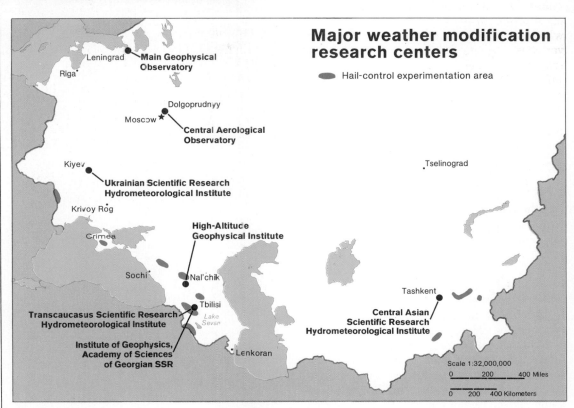

Major weather modification research centers

⬮ Hail-control experimentation area

Leningrad · Main Geophysical Observatory
Riga
Dolgoprudnyy
Moscow ★
Central Aerological Observatory
Kiyev
Ukrainian Scientific Research Hydrometeorological Institute
Krivoy Rog
Crimea
High-Altitude Geophysical Institute
Sochi · Nal'chik
Tbilisi
Lake Sevan
Transcaucasus Scientific Research Hydrometeorological Institute
Institute of Geophysics, Academy of Sciences of Georgian SSR
Lenkoran
Tselinograd
Tashkent
Central Asian Scientific Research Hydrometeorological Institute

Scale 1:32,000,000
0   200   400 Miles
0   200   400 Kilometers

cloud growth in experiments conducted in Moldavia.

The USSR is also active in research on controlled environments. A sizable investment in greenhouses is being made in an effort to supply urban populations with fresh vegetables throughout the year. Soviet greenhouse space under glass and plastic has increased from less than 500 hectares in 1965 to more than 2,700 hectares in 1973; it is scheduled for further expansion to more than 3,300 hectares by 1975. An additional 3,000 or more hectares of controlled environment is represented by electric and manure- and fuel-heated hotbeds, cold frames (solar-heated plant beds), and various types of plastic ground cover. Hydroponic (soilless) culture and artificial lighting are used primarily for experimental purposes and for vegetable transplants in winter greenhouses.

About 80 percent of the greenhouse space is in northern and central European USSR. Greenhouses are usually part of large, specialized sovkhozes and kolkhozes located near major urban areas. Almost all winter greenhouses are constructed in standard, prefabricated units which are assembled into 6-hectare blocks or multiples thereof to minimize labor requirements and reduce construction costs per unit. Since 1970, a high priority has been placed on the construction of plastic greenhouses and ground cover since plastic is generally only 10 to 15 percent as expensive as glass. Plastic-covered areas already account for 60 percent of the vegetable production from covered areas.

Soviet production of hothouse vegetables has increased from less than 135,000 tons in 1965 to more than 350,000 tons in 1972, but less than 10 percent of that total is available during the winter months when fresh produce is in especially short supply. Cucumbers account for 55 percent and onions and tomatoes for another 35 percent of all Soviet greenhouse production. Construction of more greenhouses in southern locations (the Crimea, Sochi, Lenkoran, Uzbekistan) is planned to help diversify the winter selection and provide northern areas with more fresh vegetables during the "dead season" from November to March.

Greenhouses near Rīga

Part 3

The System

Although the differences between the environmental and technological resources of the United States and those of the USSR are many and great, the differences in agricultural management systems, the labor force, and the character of rural life appear to be even greater.

Agriculture in the USSR is divided into two sectors. The socialized sector consists of state and collective farms and accounts for more than two-thirds of agricultural production. The private sector comprises small garden plots and livestock holdings that account for the remainder of total farm output. The output of the private sector per unit of both land and labor exceeds that of the socialized sector. In an effort to improve production in the latter, social and monetary incentives have been offered to farm workers for many years; but major problems remain, and experimentation in management and organizational forms continues to occupy the attention of agricultural policymakers. The giant state farms, which have been increasing in numbers as collective farms have been converted to this form of management, still produce well below expectations despite their centralized control, economies of scale, and relatively better technology.

The proportion of the population living in the countryside and working in agriculture is far greater in the USSR than in the United States. Soviet agriculture remains extremely labor-intensive, in contrast to capital-intensive U.S. farm operations. This difference will gradually lessen as industrialization and urbanization continue to draw migrants from rural areas and mechanization releases more and more farm labor. The rate of migration, however, will vary greatly from one part of the country to another because of linguistic, demographic, and economic differences.

The nature of rural settlement also differs: most U.S. farmsteads are dispersed, single-family units whose inhabitants travel into town for entertainment and shopping; in the USSR most rural settlement consists of villages whose inhabitants disperse daily to tend the outlying fields. This difference is being intensified by Soviet efforts to consolidate the smallest villages into larger towns with housing and other amenities more comparable to those in cities.

Diffusion of knowledge and information among the rural population in the USSR tends to be less rapid than in the United States because educational levels are lower and information less accessible. Despite continuing improvement in extension of educational opportunities, this situation will continue to impede the system as efforts are made to assimilate new technology.

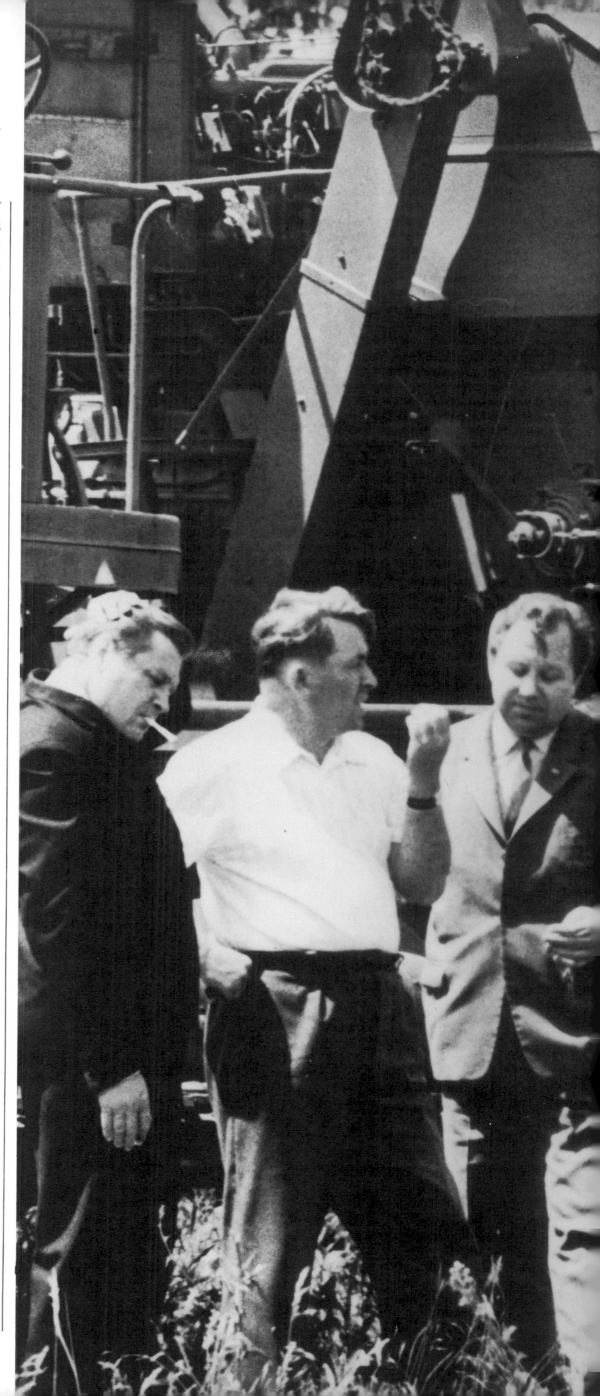

Management

Management of Soviet agriculture begins in the Communist Party's Politburo, where spokesmen for the agricultural sector contend with representatives of other interests—chiefly defense and industry—for the allocation of the USSR's investment resources. Decisions at this level inevitably have a political component. Agriculture has played a pivotal role in Soviet internal politics since Stalin's death, and failure of programs or particularly poor harvests have contributed to the downfall of senior Soviet officials, most notably Malenkov and Khrushchev. Brezhnev, as did Khrushchev, pays close heed to agriculture and has initiated major new farm programs.

From the Politburo, lines of authority extend through the Party Secretariat and its subordinate Department for Agriculture, through republic and oblast committees (obkom), to the rayon party committee (raykom). At the lowest level is the party committee for an individual farm. A parallel control channel in the state administrative apparatus originates in the USSR Council of Ministers and extends through the USSR Ministry of Agriculture to the union republic agricultural ministries and ultimately to agricultural administrations at the oblast and rayon levels.

The Ministry of Agriculture is only one of a number of central ministries which have operating responsibilities in Soviet agriculture. It oversees the production of crops and livestock, directs the state and collective farm systems, and supports research facilities. The Ministry of Procurement is of comparable importance. It buys for the state much of the production of various crops and also livestock for slaughter, milk, eggs, and wool, and directs milling, the storage of grain and flour, and the manufacture of mixed feeds. Other ministries supervise food processing, livestock slaughter, land reclamation, and agricultural machine building. These divisions are not reflected in the party's Department for Agriculture, which has a supervisory role over the entire agricultural spectrum.

Party and state roles interlock throughout agricultural administration but all major decisions and initiatives are reserved to the Party. Agricultural programs are laid down at the inception of Five-Year Plan periods and at Party Congresses. Special plenums of the Party's Central Committee may be convened to receive the announcement of yet another program or to provide a forum for criticism of agricultural failures. All key positions in the state agricultural bureaucracy and in the vast collective farm system down to the level of kolkhoz chairman are held by Party members. At the grassroot level, Party committees for individual farms whip up enthusiasm for production drives and spark hikes in pledges for production targets.

The Ministry of Agriculture is organized along conventional lines comparable to Western administrative organizations. It has undergone periodic changes in size and re-organizations of responsibilities. Stalin favored highly centralized administration and during his tenure the Ministry was dominant vis-a-vis Party agricultural cadres. Khrushchev found all central ministries stultified and largely stripped them of their functions, which were parceled out to regional organizations. Party cadres were instructed to become specialists in industry and agriculture and to increase their activities in and control over these sectors. After Khrushchev's fall, the central ministries, including the Ministry

of Agriculture, were rehabilitated, and centralized administration was once more in vogue. The Ministry is now made up of some 19 separate administrations, 10 of which follow production in major crop and animal husbandry categories while the remainder are charged with functional responsibilities in such areas as finance and planning.

Although Brezhnev does not share Khrushchev's compulsion for frequent drastic overhauling of the machinery of agricultural administration, he has long been critical of the agricultural bureaucracy. Characterizing agricultural administration at the national and republic levels as overly complex, he has called for streamlined and simplified structures without loss of centralized guidance. Economic incentives, rather than administrative decree, are to be used to spur the formation of agro-industrial associations and interfarm organizations.

Whatever the success of the new programs, the Brezhnev regime remains firmly committed to heavy investment in the agricultural sector. This orientation contrasts with the situation under Stalin when the agricultural sector was stripped to provide funds for industrial growth. Stalin's successors have shown a greater awareness of the degree to which overall economic growth has been hindered by agricultural shortcomings and have initiated, or at least identified themselves with, reforms and innovations intended to expand production and strengthen the farm sector generally. Some, such as the New Lands development, have succeeded, while others have been essentially poorly conceived and short lived panaceas, as was Khrushchev's corn program. More lasting has been the income revolution of the last decade, which has improved the quality of life in the Soviet countryside.

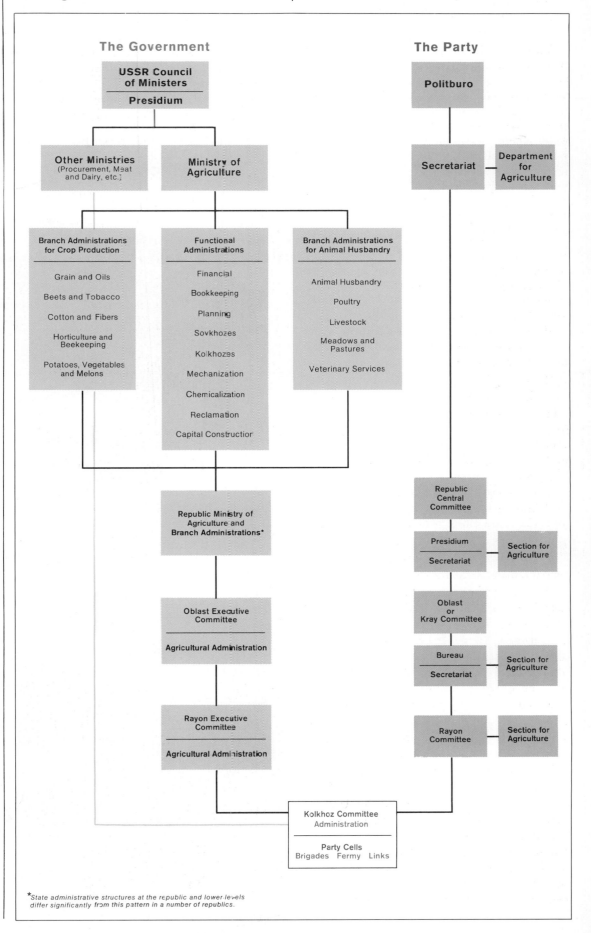

*State administrative structures at the republic and lower levels differ significantly from this pattern in a number of republics.

Rural Population

The rural population of the USSR in 1973 was 102 million persons. Although declining in recent decades, the proportion of the total USSR population living in the countryside (41 percent) is still far greater than in the United States. Similarly, the number of people directly employed in agriculture is much greater—slightly more than a quarter of the total Soviet labor force compared to 5 percent in the United States.

Although there has been a stream of migration from rural to urban areas in the USSR ever since the country began to industrialize, many rural areas are still overpopulated. Programs to move farm workers to the eastern part of the country and to reclaimed areas have not been entirely successful, and the regional distribution of rural manpower remains poorly fitted to agricultural labor requirements. Farm labor is plentiful in most parts of the Ukraine, North Caucasus, Moldavia, Transcaucasus, and Central Asia; but it is short supply in the Central and Northwest Regions, Urals, East Siberia, and the Far East. Yet, outmigration from these areas continues because living conditions are so poor. The seasonal fluctuation in agricultural manpower requirements creates another problem, which is alleviated by the mobilization during the harvest season of factory workers, youth, and military units.

The migration from labor-deficient areas has occurred despite improvements in the living conditions of agricultural workers—through pensions, higher wages, bonus plans, paid vacations, health benefits, and housing grants. To make matters worse, the first to move out are likely to be the more highly skilled and younger people. Many young men do not return to live in their villages after military service. There is also a tendency for those who do migrate to Siberia to return to the west in a few years or to move into the cities, where labor is also in demand and higher industrial wages are available.

Central Asia is particularly marked by excess population in rural areas. Lack of modern technical skills and the linguistic and cultural differences of the Turkic-speaking peoples serve as a barrier to outmigration to the Slavic-speaking areas where agricultural labor is in short supply. The birth rate among the rural population of Central Asia is the highest in the USSR, and the rural population there is growing most rapidly.

Educational levels, although rising, are substantially lower in the countryside than in the urban areas. Work-training programs in agriculture-related skills are currently being emphasized for rural youth.

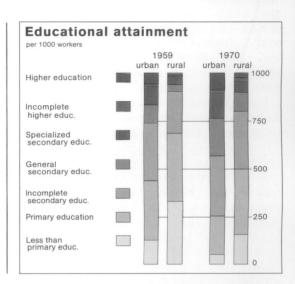

Educational attainment

per 1000 workers

Rural population as a proportion of total population-1973

60% or more
40-59%
0-39%

Scale 1:60,000,000

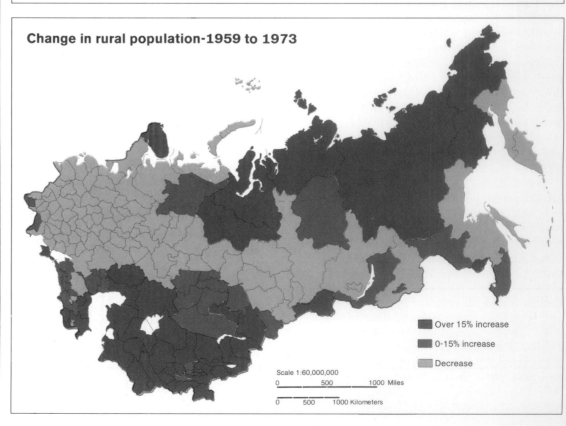

Change in rural population-1959 to 1973

Over 15% increase
0-15% increase
Decrease

Scale 1:60,000,000

Rural population and agricultural manpower

millions

Total population

Rural population

Total agricultural workers

Kolkhoz workers

Sovkhoz workers

Rural Settlement

An important aspect of Soviet efforts to transform and modernize the farm sector of the economy is the restructuring of rural settlement. Although Leninist ideology has long called for the equalization of "material and social conditions" of the rural peasants and urban workers, living conditions in most Soviet villages—when measured against those in the cities—continue to fall short in terms of housing, cultural and educational opportunity, recreation, and the availability of consumer goods.

The character of rural settlement differs greatly from one part of the USSR to another, reflecting the historical diversity of various regions. The predominant pattern was set by the large Slavic agricultural villages throughout the steppes, which average several hundred inhabitants. Agricultural settlements in the forest steppe and other northern and eastern areas tend to be smaller, but villages still prevail over individual farmsteads. The pattern of widely separated individual farmsteads, familiar in the United States, is found only in the Baltic republics. For example, in Latvia in 1970 there were 74,461 rural populated places with 5 or fewer inhabitants and only 1 village with more than 2,000 people. In contrast, in the Moldavian SSR, the average rural village has more than 1,000 inhabitants. The labor-intensive irrigated and oasis agriculture of the arid Central Asian region is also marked by large settlements although in the mountains tiny villages are numerous.

Since the early days of Soviet rule there have been proposals for the elimination of individual farmsteads and those small villages that are located away from transport lines or are in other ways disadvantaged. Khrushchev's controversial promotion of *agrogorods* highlighted the development of large urbanized settlements for agricultural workers in the late 1950's. During the 1960's and continuing until the present, a concerted effort has been made to restructure and improve rural settlements and living conditions.

Plans developed in the 1960's earmarked 110,000 rural settlements—about 16 percent of those existing at that time—for long-term development. The remainder apparently are to be eliminated or allowed to stagnate. Current plans for individual oblasts and republics show similarly ambitious, and probably unrealistic, goals for reduction in the number of villages. For example, the plan for Smolensk Oblast calls for 1,500 large settlements to accommodate those now living in some 7,000 villages which have no more than 10 families each. Belorussia is attempting to reduce some 27,000 small villages to about 5,000 large settlements. These plans are controversial for both political and economic reasons, and there is disagreement on how far and how fast they should be pushed.

The larger settlements are being expanded with new standardized housing for the resettled inhabitants of the small villages. Many of the designs are for detached houses, but apartment dwellings—similar in appearance to low-rise construction in Scandinavia—are also being constructed in large numbers in farm communities. The latter accommodations are designed especially for young couples and small families as part of the effort to stem the exodus of young people from the countryside. Financial incentives are part of the resettlement programs. In Latvia, for example, where efforts are being made to speed up rural reconstruction, the USSR Gosbank (State Bank) will extend credits to kolkhozes and to individuals through kolkhozes and sovkhozes to build housing at specified rural population points. Loans are made for 15 years with repayment beginning after 5 years.

In addition to better housing, the new consolidated villages are designed to provide the kinds of cultural and service facilities hitherto lacking in the countryside. Each village will have paved roads, central water supply, and sewer facilities, and agriculture-related industrial facilities may be included. A variety of plans for model settlements have been drawn up, and some new villages have already been constructed.

Between 1960 and 1970, the number of rural populated places declined in all parts of the USSR. Progress in consolidation has been rapid (54 percent) in the Far East Region, especially in the Yakut ASSR, where many tiny reindeer herders' settlements were consolidated without much difficulty, but the total number of people involved is very small. Consolidation has been slow in the densely settled Baltic and Transcaucasus republics, as low as 2 percent in the Georgian SSR. In these areas, strong commitment to traditional ways of life as well as outright resistance based on nationalistic sentiments make consolidation more difficult.

The new large villages can more easily supply amenities and utilities not now available to the rural population, and the elimination of small villages simplifies the Soviet administrative structure. However, the average distance to work in the fields is greatly increased, and the individual farmer's sense of identification with the land is reduced even further. The current ambitious plans for consolidation may never be fully realized because of the great costs and the resistance of the rural population.

New rural housing in Latvia

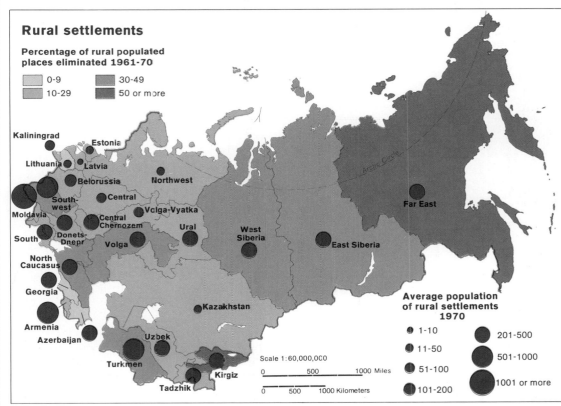

Rural settlements

Percentage of rural populated places eliminated 1961-70

0-9
10-29
30-49
50 or more

Average population of rural settlements 1970

1-10
11-50
51-100
101-200
201-500
501-1000
1001 or more

Scale 1:60,000,000

0   500   1000 Miles
0   500   1000 Kilometers

Organizational Forms

The reorganization of agriculture by the Bolsheviks got under way with the nationalization of all land in 1918, but for the next decade most farmers continued to operate their holdings independently. By 1927 only 2 percent of the peasantry was enrolled in the socialized sector, made up of state farms and several types of cooperative farms. Change came abruptly with Stalin's call in 1928—the first year of the First Five-Year Plan—for all-out collectivization. Peasants were forced to join collective farms (kolkhozes), and independent farmers were destroyed as a class; at the end of the drive only about 5 percent of all farmland remained in private operation. In addition to meeting the political goal of eliminating individual enterprises, collectivization established the basis for industrialization: the state was able to create capital through purchase of agricultural products from the newly formed kolkhozes at artificially low prices.

A kolkhoz is a cooperative organization of farm families granted perpetual rights to rent-free state land. Sovkhozes are state enterprises that, in the Soviet view, are rural equivalents of urban industries. Of the two systems, the sovkhoz is more compatible with communist ideology. Kolkhozes have always been viewed as a transitional form, essentially a compromise which brought farm families into the socialized sector while permitting them a measure of private enterprise.

Before World War II, kolkhozes were small units averaging fewer than 100 families, but post-war amalgamation programs reduced their number and increased their size. Between 1958 and 1972 the number of kolkhozes declined by more than half—from 67,700 to 32,300—through conversion of kolkhozes to sovkhozes and the continuing amalgamation of smaller kolkhozes. Sovkhozes, which increased in number from 6,000 to 15,500 in the same period, are generally much larger. By 1971 total kolkhoz and sovkhoz cultivated areas had reached parity.

The emphasis now appears to be on reducing the differences between the two systems. Sovkhozes are shifting to cost accounting, a system which has always been in effect on kolkhozes, while kolkhozes have been required since 1967 to follow the sovkhoz practice of paying monthly cash wages.

With the strong endorsement of high Soviet leaders, agricultural managers have instituted innovative specialization programs to improve farm efficiency. Inter-kolkhoz, inter-sovkhoz, kolkhoz-sovkhoz, and agro-industrial associations are well advanced in Moldavia, Belorussia, the Ukraine, and several regions of the RSFSR. In a typical inter-kolkhoz association member farms pool resources to operate such specialized functions as fodder production, cattle breeding, or fattening of animals. These associations also exploit timber resources, produce building materials, process food, and provide repair services. A typical agro-industrial association would integrate sugar beet farms and factories as well as livestock farms, which fatten cattle on the factory wastes. To join an association, a farm must pay an initiation fee and a fixed annual contribution, which tends to exclude poorer farms from membership.

Working units in kolkhozes and sovkhozes are of three main types—the brigade, the *ferma,* and the *zveno* (link). The brigade is the basic work force of the kolkhoz. Its equivalent in the sovkhoz system is the *otdeleniye* (section). Brigades generally have permanently assigned personnel and management and are organized on a territorial basis, but they may be formed for specific tasks and dissolved upon their completion. Often a brigade will be based on one or more of the villages which made up a small kolkhoz prior to its amalgamation with neighboring kolkhozes. The predominant type is the comprehensive brigade, which produces a mix of crops and livestock.

A *ferma* is a production unit that specializes in meat, poultry, or dairy products. It has permanently assigned specialist personnel and fixed facilities which may include barns, cattle pens and feed lots, and machinery. It may be assigned to a brigade or section or administered by the farm central management.

A *zveno* (link) is a small team that is usually assigned responsibility for a designated area and crop from earliest cultivation to final harvest. In recent years, controversy has surrounded the development of mechanized links—teams of specialists equipped with tractors, who are paid on the basis of crop yields rather than work time. Party ideologues object to their high incomes and their independent work practices, which smack too much of free enterprise. Nevertheless, the link system continues to make headway. Proponents cite dramatic production increases compared to the output of more conventionally organized work forces. Some have even called for the elimination of brigades and sections, together with their administrative staffs, leaving self-supervising links to conclude contracts with the farm and to work directly under the farm's chief agronomist.

The socialized sector is supplied by Selkhoztekhnika (Agricultural Equipment Supply Agency), which sells tractors, machinery, and agricultural chemicals to sovkhozes and kolkhozes. Branch offices, located at each *rayon* center, maintain specialists and facilities for installation, servicing, and repair, and provide transport and other services. Heavy equipment for road building and land reclamation, which would be uneconomical for farms to purchase and maintain, is provided, together with crews, on a contract basis. Selkhoztekhnika replaces the Machine Tractor Stations—abolished in 1958—which supplied and maintained all farm machinery and equipment and performed much of the plowing, sowing, and harvesting work on kolkhozes.

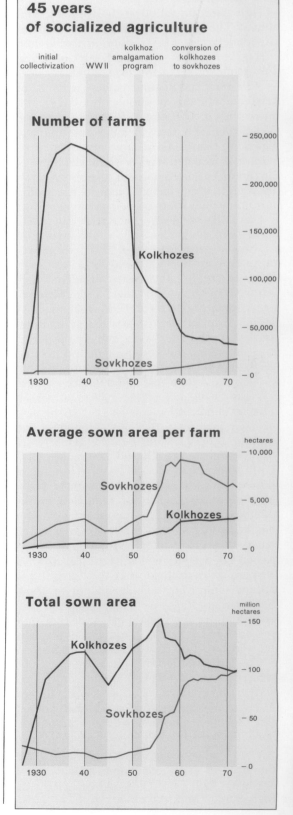

45 years of socialized agriculture

initial collectivization | WWII | kolkhoz amalgamation program | conversion of kolkhozes to sovkhozes

Number of farms

Kolkhozes

Sovkhozes

Average sown area per farm hectares

Sovkhozes

Kolkhozes

Total sown area million hectares

Kolkhozes

Sovkhozes

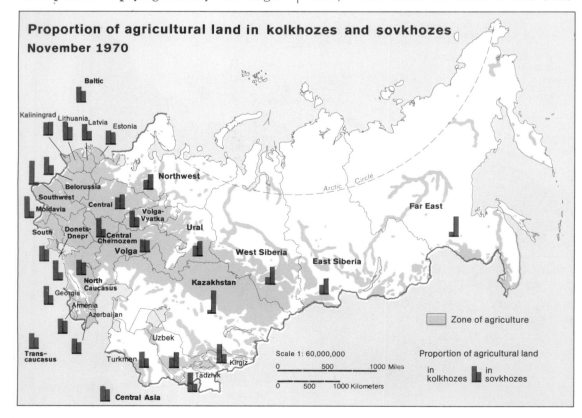

Proportion of agricultural land in kolkhozes and sovkhozes November 1970

Baltic
Kaliningrad Lithuania Latvia Estonia
Northwest
Belorussia
Southwest
Moldavia Central
Volga-Vyatka
Donets-Dnepr Ural
South Central Chernozem
Volga
Far East
West Siberia
East Siberia
North Caucasus Kazakhstan
Georgia
Armenia
Azerbaijan
Uzbek
Trans-caucasus
Turkmen Kirgiz
Tadzhik
Central Asia

Arctic Circle

Zone of agriculture

Scale 1 : 60,000,000
0   500   1000 Miles
0   500   1000 Kilometers

Proportion of agricultural land
in kolkhozes   in sovkhozes

The Collective Farm

The individual kolkhoz (contraction of *kollektivnoye khozyaystvo*—collective farm) differs little in form and function from its prototype of 1918. It remains an agricultural cooperative whose member families share profits among themselves and, in theory at least, run the farm's affairs on a democratic basis. Despite the ideological fervor implicit in such kolkhoz names as "Banner of the Soviets" and "Road to Communism," the kolkhoz is a conservative community, resisting change and maintaining traditional values.

The key element in the kolkhoz is the family, which consists of the kolkhoznik, his wife (also a full member of the kolkhoz) and children, and several older relatives perhaps retired on pension. Membership in the kolkhoz is a family birthright: children are ordinarily enrolled as full members when they reach age 16. Transfer of membership from one kolkhoz to another occurs occasionally, usually as a consequence of a marriage. Few Soviet citizens leave other occupations for the rigors of kolkhoz life.

Most kolkhoz families live in individual cottages, usually with a fenced garden plot located to the rear. A kolkhoz may comprise as many as several thousand households but on the average there are 440 per kolkhoz clustered in several villages. Surrounding the villages are the communally worked fields.

A kolkhoznik is expected to work full time with his brigade, at least during busy periods, and he may be penalized if he fails to put in the minimum number of workdays required by the kolkhoz. If qualified, he may be assigned to a tractor or machine maintenance team or to a *ferma*. Males tend to hold down the better paid jobs while women do a disproportionate share of the unskilled field work. Many kolkhozes operate subsidiary enterprises such as food processing and construction materials plants which provide work during slack periods. Occasionally a kolkhoz may find itself short of labor, and a harried chairman must bid for non-kolkhoz labor with cash inducements.

Wages are based on either time or piecework, with bonuses for production that exceeds the goals of the kolkhoz plan. In 1972 the average kolkhoznik took home slightly more than 4 rubles a day in a combination of cash and payment in kind, almost three times the rate for 1960. This still lags well behind the pay of the industrial worker, but the combined income of a kolkhoznik and his family, supplemented by the produce of their private plot, provides an adequate living for all and may permit an occasional luxury. A portion of the wages is paid in cash on a guaranteed monthly basis, in effect an advance on the kolkhoznik's anticipated annual earnings. The kolkhoz extends loans to members for the construction of new homes and makes building materials available if resources permit.

The kolkhoznik's life is enmeshed in rules and goals, and his activities are scrutinized by a hierarchy of organizations. Each kolkhoz is governed by a charter patterned closely on the general kolkhoz charter but with some attention to local conditions. The General Meeting is, in theory, the highest administrative body in the kolkhoz, and all members are expected to participate in its quarterly sessions. Real control is exercised by the *raykom*, the Communist Party district committee. It selects the kolkhoz chairman, invariably a party member, who is given pro forma approval by the General Meeting. Today most kolkhoz chairmen have good

technical backgrounds as well as correct party credentials. Party members also dominate the nine-man kolkhoz board and brigade staffs.

Motivation of the kolkhoznik, who tends to proceed at his own pace, can be a trial for management. The Soviet press regularly condemns kolkhozniks who contribute less than the required number of workdays, keep privately owned stock in excess of the maximum permitted, and engage in illegal sales of kolkhoz produce. Particular outrage is vented on the kolkhoz chairman who is found guilty of complicity in these schemes.

Despite the rise in incomes over the last decade, living conditions for most kolkhozniks remain far behind those of the city-dweller. The typical small, wooden cottages are generally lacking in indoor plumbing and central heating. Telephones are not yet common. Village streets are unpaved and virtually impassable to automobiles and small trucks during spring rains. Most rural homes are electrified, however, and TV sets are becoming increasingly available.

Rastsvet, a prosperous kolkhoz center in Odessa Oblast, has modern housing, a House of Culture, school, restaurant, and stores

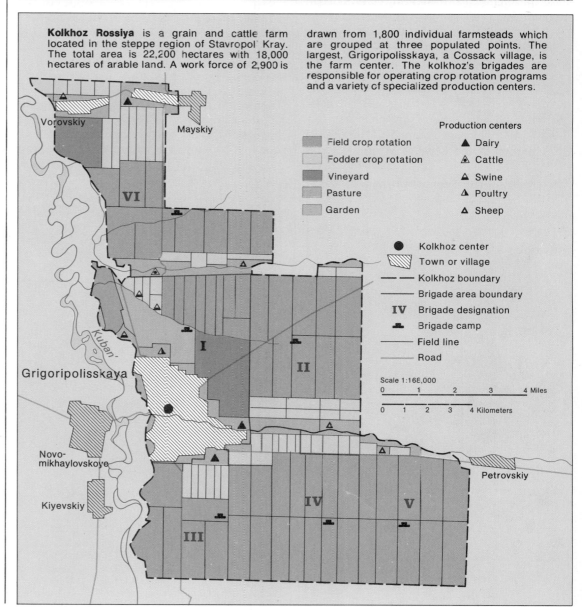

Kolkhoz Rossiya is a grain and cattle farm located in the steppe region of Stavropol' Kray. The total area is 22,200 hectares with 18,000 hectares of arable land. A work force of 2,900 is drawn from 1,800 individual farmsteads which are grouped at three populated points. The largest, Grigoripolisskaya, a Cossack village, is the farm center. The kolkhoz's brigades are responsible for operating crop rotation programs and a variety of specialized production centers.

	Production centers
Field crop rotation	▲ Dairy
Fodder crop rotation	⬤ Cattle
Vineyard	△ Swine
Pasture	△ Poultry
Garden	△ Sheep

● Kolkhoz center
▨ Town or village
– – – Kolkhoz boundary
—— Brigade area boundary
IV Brigade designation
⚓ Brigade camp
—— Field line
—— Road

Scale 1:168,000
0   1   2   3   4 Miles
0 1 2 3 4 Kilometers

Private Holdings

Almost 30 percent of Soviet agricultural output originates in the private sector, and most observers acknowledge that—although generally higher in price—it is superior in quality to the output of the socialized sector. Private holdings continue to be tolerated by the regime out of practical necessity, although their existence remains distasteful to the more doctrinaire Soviet ideologues.

The right to farm a private plot (subsidiary farming, in Soviet terminology) is granted to a vast number of Soviet citizens, including kolkhoz and sovkhoz workers, various categories of rural specialists such as teachers and administrators, and even urban workers. The produce of the plots is mainly for the personal use of the farmer and his family but may be sold in the kolkhoz markets. The maximum size of a holding, strictly controlled by statute, has varied but now is one-half hectare, including land under dwellings and outbuildings. If the land is irrigated, the maximum permitted shrinks to 0.2 hectare. No private farmer may hire labor.

The bulk of private farming is done by kolkhoz residents. The plot is usually worked by a kolkhoznik's wife, children, and older relatives. The plot also sometimes competes for the kolkhoznik's time and energies, creating problems for the farm chairman or brigade leader, who must maintain adequate work forces in the socialized sector.

The private plots of the kolkhozniks are generally contiguous to their dwellings and closely resemble U.S. kitchen gardens. The kolkhoz family usually owns its dwelling, outbuildings, and tools—and may sell them—but holds no legal title of ownership to the private plot, which is assigned to the family by resolution of the General Meeting of the kolkhoz. Its size may vary within the half-hectare limit depending on the number of people in the family and the extent of their labor contribution to the kolkhoz. Traditionally a plot remains with a family through the generations, provided a member remains active in the kolkhoz. Even a kolkhoz pensioner living alone may continue to farm a private plot. The right to use the plot can be withdrawn, however, if it is not farmed for two successive years or if there have been irregularities in its operation.

The kolkhoz family concentrates its private farming on high-value, labor-intensive crops and livestock products such as potatoes, vegetables, fruit, meat, milk, and eggs. While only 3 percent of the total sown area of the USSR is privately cultivated, it has been estimated that as much as one-fifth of the total arable land—pasture, hayland, and sown area—is utilized to support the private sector's output of livestock products. Kolkhozniks usually graze their animals on the common pasture lands of the kolkhoz and unused land such as railroad rights-of-way. They may purchase feed from the kolkhoz or take feed as payment in kind for labor.

Privately held animals constitute a decreasing proportion of all livestock in the USSR because the farm population is declining, there are restrictions on the number of animals a farmer may keep, and at the same time state herds are being expanded rapidly. The Kolkhoz Model Charter authorizes a family to keep a cow, a sow, and as many as 10 sheep or goats. A calf may be kept as long as two years. Larger numbers of livestock are permitted in areas where animal husbandry is the predominant form of production. No limits are set on poultry or rabbit stocks. Normally, animal holdings peak at mid-year through the addition of offspring and by purchases of young stock from the kolkhoz. These animals are fattened and then sold off before winter to minimize maintenance costs.

Sovkhoz workers farm their private plots in much the same manner as kolkhozniks; however, their allotments are usually smaller in size. Urban workers may receive small allotments on nearby lands assigned to their factories or offices, or on other vacant lands within or near the city. Large tracts of these miniscule private plots, similar in appearance to the World War II victory gardens in the United States, are interspersed with housing developments in all Soviet cities and towns or are situated on lands just outside urban limits. Each plot is equipped with a small shed used for tools and temporary residence. The plots provide urban dwellers with a recreational outlet as well as substantial supplies of vegetables and fruits.

For many years, private holdings were the major and often the only source of a kolkhoznik's cash income. As income for kolkhoz and sovkhoz workers rises, there is less incentive for the individual to exploit the private plot to the maximum. As late as 1972, however, private farming supplied 62 percent of the potatoes, almost half of the eggs, 36 percent of the vegetables, and 34 percent of the milk and meat produced. Any attempt to curtail so large a sector of the economy would drastically disrupt the supply of food to the Soviet population.

Well kept private plots adjoin the recently constructed cottages of Sovkhoz Chaplinskiy near Kherson in the Ukraine

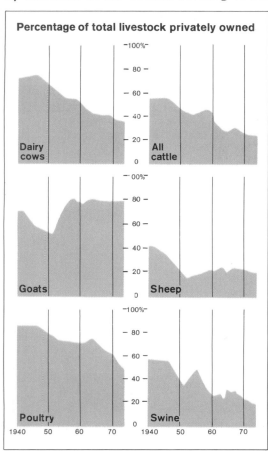

Percentage of total livestock privately owned

Dairy cows / All cattle

Goats / Sheep

Poultry / Swine

1940 50 60 70   1940 50 60 70

The State Farm

The sovkhoz (contraction of *sovetskoye khozyaystvo*—state farm) differs fundamentally in organization and purpose from the kolkhoz, although in appearance and layout it is often indistinguishable. The sovkhoz is a state enterprise. Its workers are state employees, and their wages are paid from state funds. All means of production are state property. Farm directors are appointed by the *rayon* agricultural administration, subject, of course, to Communist Party approval.

The first sovkhozes were formed in 1918 from expropriated landlords' estates. From the outset, they were intended to serve as examples for kolkhozes and independent farmers, demonstrating advanced, scientific farming techniques and emphasizing the high return in labor productivity gained from large-scale mechanized farming. They were also to specialize in the production of high-quality foodstuffs for nearby urban centers.

Results were slow in coming. In the first decade of Soviet rule, sovkhozes remained few in number, relatively small in size, and negligible in their contribution to total agricultural output. For many years sovkhozes had to be shored up with state subsidies.

Sovkhozes nearly tripled in number during the collectivization drive of the early 1930's. During Khrushchev's push into the New Lands in 1953-55, most of the territory newly claimed for agriculture in northern Kazakhstan was given over to sovkhozes. A further threefold increase came in the late 1950's and 1960's, when many kolkhozes, particularly weaker ones, were combined and converted to sovkhozes. At the same time, financial restructuring helped improve the position of the sovkhoz vis-a-vis the kolkhoz. Although subsidies were phased out, the prices paid by state procurement agencies for mandatory deliveries were increased, but not quite to the level of those paid to kolkhozes. By the end of 1975, when both systems will have fully gone over to cost accounting, prices will be uniform.

Sovkhozes operating on a cost-accounting basis are expected to show a profit. Deliveries are made to government procurement organizations at prices fixed by the state. Individual sovkhozes can conclude contracts for sale of surplus produce, and a portion of a farm's profits can be retained for local improvements. Sovkhoz workers draw monthly wages based, for the most part, on standard government-established piece rates, which vary according to the importance and arduousness of the task. At the end of the agricultural year bonuses are divided among sovkhoz workers for production in excess of the farm's goal.

Sovkhozes are generally larger and better equipped than kolkhozes although they tend to be less intensively cultivated. In 1972 the average sovkhoz employed almost 600 workers in all phases of its operations, including management, services, and subsidiary industries. Average sovkhoz size was about 20,000 hectares, with slightly more than 6,000 sown to crops.

Sovkhozes tend to specialize to a greater extent than do kolkhozes. Dairy and dairy/beef farms together make up slightly more than 40 percent of all sovkhozes. Grain sovkhozes are fewer in number but are massive production units with sown areas averaging about 20,000 hectares. Many sovkhozes have been set up near large cities to facilitate the supply of milk, eggs, poultry, vegetables, and potatoes to urban populations.

Larger sovkhozes are divided into a number of *otdeleniya* (sections)—production subdivisions with fixed boundaries, permanently assigned workers and specialists, and the necessary equipment. Field brigades are responsible for all agricultural work on the land assigned to them by the section management. In smaller sovkhozes *otdeleniya* may be absent, with field brigades operating directly under control of the sovkhoz central management.

A sovkhoz center in Kostroma Oblast

Number of sovkhozes

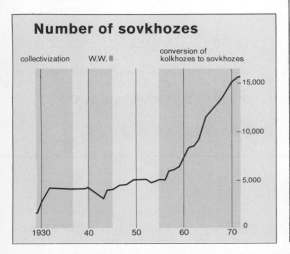

collectivization W.W. II conversion of kolkhozes to sovkhozes

15,000
10,000
5,000
0

1930   40   50   60   70

A sovkhoz in transition

Sovkhoz Kashirskiy, a hundred kilometers south of Moscow, has 6,700 hectares of agricultural land and supplies vegetables, potatoes, and milk to the Moscow market. Founded in 1919 on an expropriated estate, it has grown by absorbing weak neighboring kolkhozes and is now slated for further transformation. Small villages are being removed and new housing constructed at the sovkhoz center at Taraskovo. Section boundaries will be realigned, and the number of sections may be reduced. The sovkhoz work force will number 925 persons, with a total farm population of about 3,250.

Arable land	Pasture
Hay	Garden
Woodland	

Consolidated village	Village to be removed
● Sovkhoz center	Section center
– – Sovkhoz boundary	Section boundary
— Road or lane	IV Section number

Scale 1:106,000
0   1   2   3 Miles
0   1   2   3 Kilometers

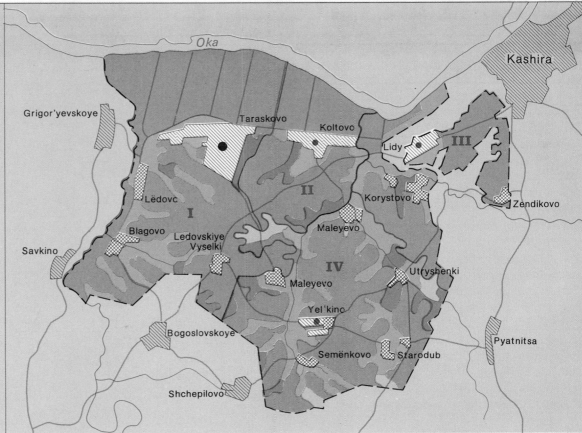

Oka

Kashira

Grigor'yevskoye

Taraskovo

Koltovo

Lidy

III

Lëdovo

I

II

Korystovo

Zendikovo

Blagovo

Ledovskiye Vyselki

Maleyevo

Savkino

IV

Maleyevo

Utryshenki

Yel'kino

Bogoslovskoye

Semënkovo   Starodub

Pyatnitsa

Shchepilovo

Part 4
Production

The USSR is one of the world's important food producers, ranking first in production of such crops as wheat, barley, potatoes, and sugar beets. It is less outstanding in terms of overall farm output and yields because of environmental limitations, managerial inefficiencies, and levels of applied technology lower than those in Western Europe and the United States.

The growth of Soviet crop production in the 1950's was heavily dependent on increases in sown area; since then, yield improvements have been the main factor in expanded output. More fertilizer, better plant varieties, more agricultural machinery, better tillage practices, and greater incentives for agricultural workers and managers have all contributed to increased output per hectare. Average crop production in 1969-73 was 36 percent above the average production in 1961-65, and well ahead of the 15-percent population growth during the same period.

Bread grains and potatoes are preponderant among Soviet crops; feed grains, particularly corn, dominate U.S. output. Soviet output of higher quality foods, particularly meat and fruits, is well below that of the United States. The suitability of the United States for corn is a distinct natural advantage, since corn is relatively high yielding compared to wheat and is an excellent livestock feed. Barley and rye, which do grow well under Soviet climatic conditions, are much more important there than in the United States. The current effort to boost meat and egg production by increasing the number and, more important, by raising the productivity of animals will also require raising output of feed grains and fodder crops.

Throughout its history, the USSR has had difficulty in maintaining a food supply sufficient for its population, and there have been years of extreme shortages, even famine. While it seems unlikely that shortages of this magnitude will occur again, the pressures to raise production will be relentless because of population growth, demands for a higher protein diet, and increasing food needs in other parts of the world.

Geographically, agricultural production remains concentrated within the traditional "fertile triangle," although areas beyond are now making a healthy contribution. The New Lands program extended the productive grain lands of the country, and Secretary Brezhnev's current program to intensify agricultural exploitation of the non-chernozem region promises a further modest shift in the regional distribution of overall production.

World Production

1971-1972 average

- ■ USSR
- ■ US
- ▫ Other
- **1** World ranking

EEC - European Economic Community
PRC - Peoples Republic of China
FRG - Federal Republic of Germany
GDR - German Democratic Republic

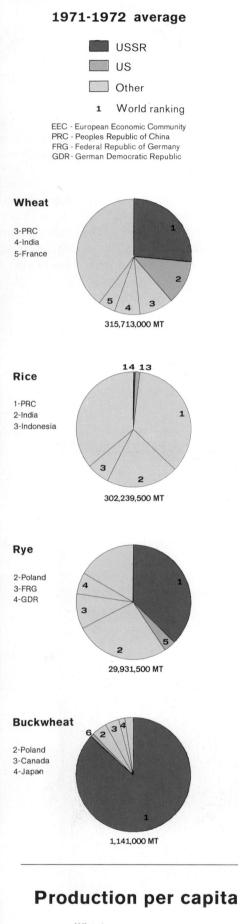

Wheat

3-PRC
4-India
5-France

315,713,000 MT

Rice

1-PRC
2-India
3-Indonesia

302,239,500 MT

Rye

2-Poland
3-FRG
4-GDR

29,931,500 MT

Buckwheat

2-Poland
3-Canada
4-Japan

1,141,000 MT

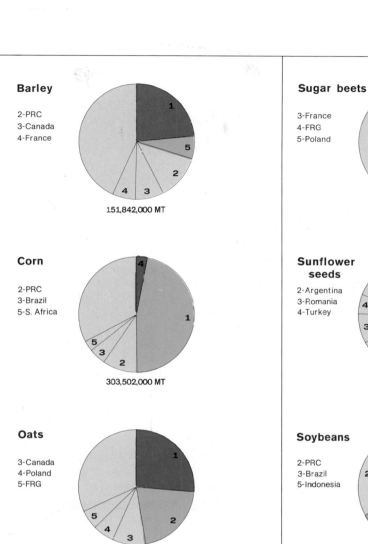

Barley

2-PRC
3-Canada
4-France

151,842,000 MT

Corn

2-PRC
3-Brazil
5-S. Africa

303,502,000 MT

Oats

3-Canada
4-Poland
5-FRG

54,513,000 MT

Millet

1-PRC
2-India
3-Nigeria

44,146,000 MT

Potatoes

2-Poland
3-PRC
4-FRG

286,419,500 MT

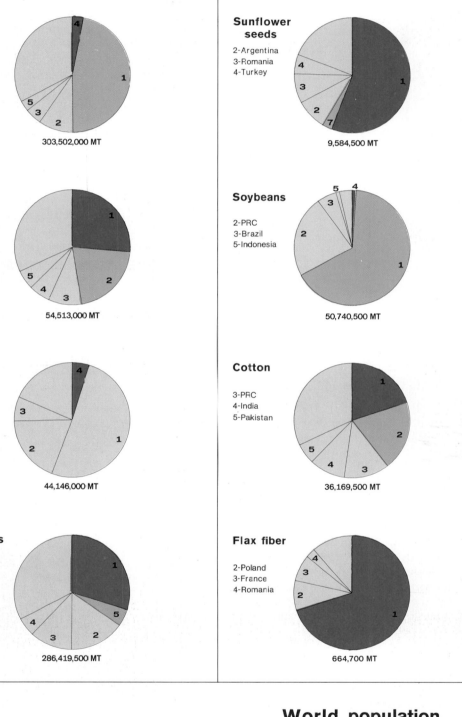

Sugar beets

3-France
4-FRG
5-Poland

235,249,500 MT

Sunflower seeds

2-Argentina
3-Romania
4-Turkey

9,584,500 MT

Soybeans

2-PRC
3-Brazil
5-Indonesia

50,740,500 MT

Cotton

3-PRC
4-India
5-Pakistan

36,169,500 MT

Flax fiber

2-Poland
3-France
4-Romania

664,700 MT

Production per capita

Wheat
- USSR — 14.4 bushels
- US — 7.7
- EEC — 5.9
- PRC — 1.1
- India — 1.6

Rice
- .36
- .94
- .18
- 5.5
- 5.2

Barley
- 8.4
- 2.0
- 6.1
- .36
- .19

Corn
- 1.8
- 26.6
- 2.3
- 1.0
- .43

World population

USSR
US
EEC
PRC
India
Africa
S. America
Other

Wheat

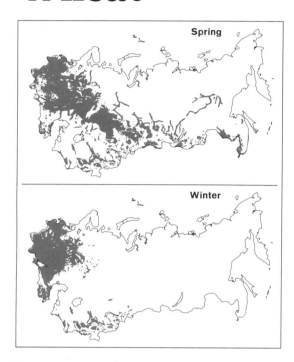

Spring

Winter

Since wheat constitutes nearly 90 percent of total Soviet food grain production and 50 percent of the total grain production, the size of the wheat harvest is an annual source of trepidation to the Soviet leadership. If the crop is poor, as it was in 1972, money may have to be spent abroad to meet consumer needs; if it is good, as in 1973, the entire economy will be bolstered. It is a sign of growing world interdependence for food supply that the size of the Soviet wheat crop has become a major source of concern in other countries as well.

The long-range trend of Soviet wheat production has been upward. The New Lands program of the 1950's added significantly to the productive grain-growing area; since then, continuing improvements in yield, based primarily on new varieties and more fertilizer, have maintained the upward trend in production despite fluctuations in sown area. But the variability of weather in the USSR is so great that the difference in output between bad years and good years is still enormous.

Spring wheat production in the New Lands has usually provided a hedge against a national wheat crop failure, because a poor harvest in the winter-wheat-growing regions of European USSR frequently is offset by a good spring wheat harvest in the New Lands and vice versa. This situation occurred most recently in 1972, although the New Lands harvest did not completely compensate for the poor harvest elsewhere.

Both winter and spring wheat are important in the USSR, but the area planted in spring wheat is about 2½ times that in winter wheat. (In the United States, conversely, the winter wheat area is more than twice that in spring wheat.) Despite the much greater area in spring wheat, the production ratio of spring to winter wheat in the USSR is only 60:40 because spring wheat yields are lower than those of winter wheat. The latter is concentrated in the western USSR, where it can withstand the winter conditions; the spring wheat belt is primarily east of the Volga, often too cold for winter crops to survive.

Average wheat yields, although fluctuating, continue to rise. Spring wheat production increased from 14 bushels per acre in 1960 to 20 bushels in 1973, compared with 21 and 29 bushels per acre for the same years in the United States. Average winter wheat yields are considerably higher, having increased from 22 bushels per acre in 1960 to 40 bushels in 1973, the latter exceeding the U.S. yield. Non-irrigated wheat yields are highest in the western areas of European USSR because of the greater soil moisture and reliability of rainfall.

Because wheat cultivation has already been extended to the limits of suitable land, the USSR must rely primarily on improving yields to increase wheat production.

Additional use of agricultural chemicals could increase yields, but neither pesticides nor fertilizer are yet available in sufficient quantities.

Wheat varieties used mainly for baking dominate Soviet wheat sowings. Durum wheat, for macaroni and similar products, is also grown—occupying 12 percent of the spring wheat area. It is grown principally in the steppe region that extends from the middle and lower Volga eastward into Kazakhstan, where climatic conditions favor high-protein durum varieties. Other species of wheat—such as turgid or rivet, club or dwarf, emmer, and spelt—are of regional and very minor importance.

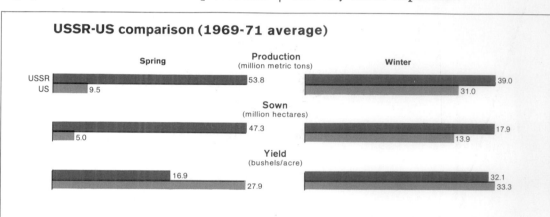

USSR-US comparison (1969-71 average)

	Spring	Production (million metric tons)	Winter
USSR		53.8	39.0
US	9.5		31.0

Sown (million hectares)

| 47.3 | | 17.9 |
| 5.0 | | 13.9 |

Yield (bushels/acre)

| 16.9 | | 32.1 |
| 27.9 | | 33.3 |

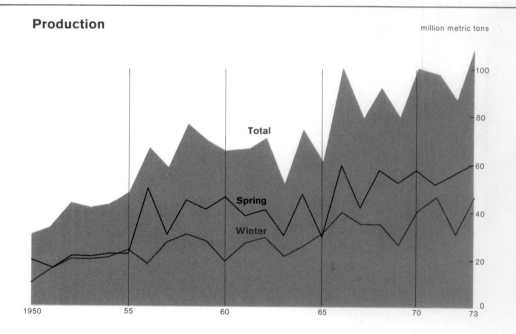

Production

million metric tons

Total

Spring

Winter

1950   55   60   65   70   73

Area sown

million hectares

Total

Spring

Winter

1950   55   60   65   70   73

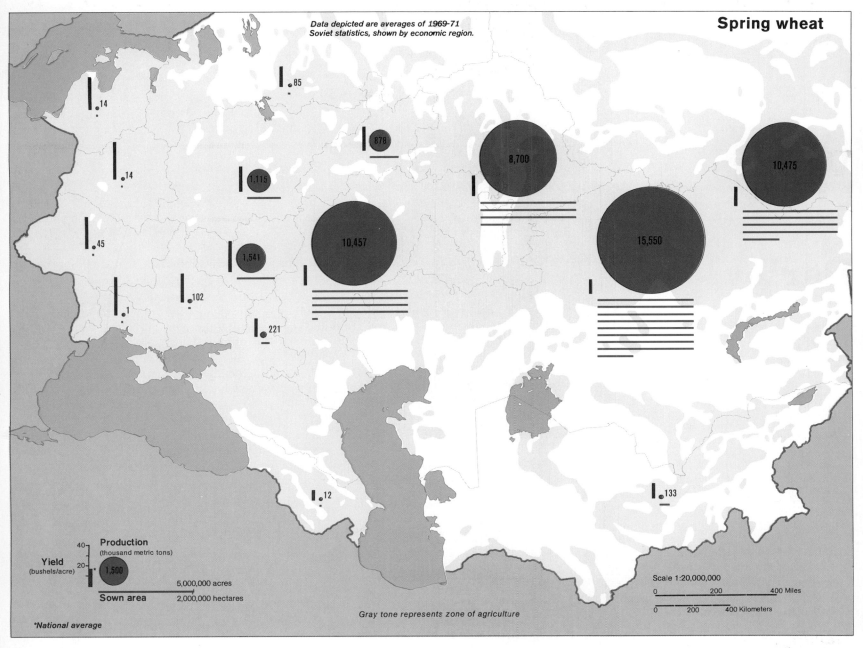

Spring wheat

Data depicted are averages of 1969-71
Soviet statistics, shown by economic region.

85

14

14

878

8,700

10,475

1,115

45

1,541

10,457

15,550

102

1

221

12

133

Production
(thousand metric tons)

Yield
(bushels/acre)

40
20

1,500

5,000,000 acres

Sown area   2,000,000 hectares

Scale 1:20,000,000

0   200   400 Miles

0   200   400 Kilometers

Gray tone represents zone of agriculture

*National average

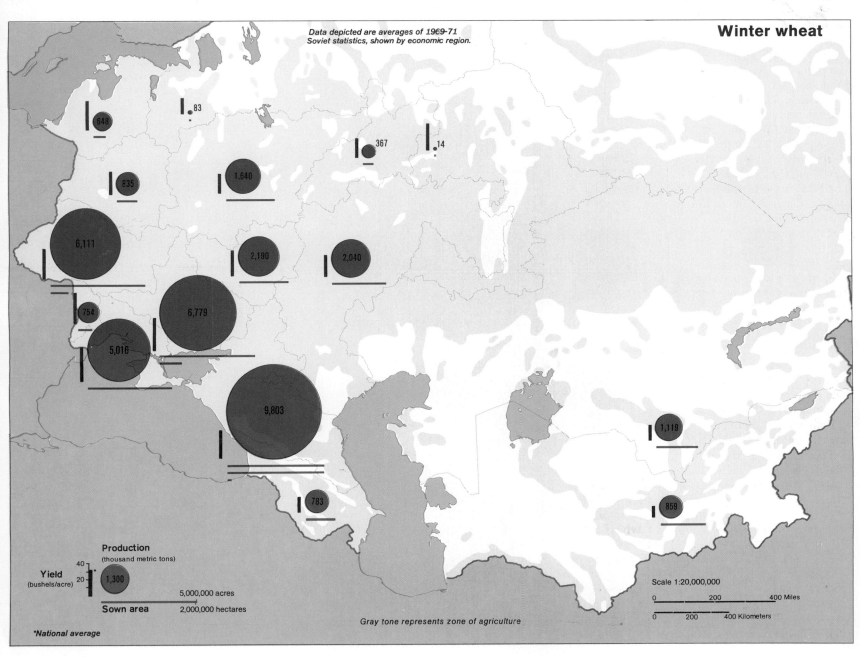

Winter wheat

Data depicted are averages of 1969-71
Soviet statistics, shown by economic region.

83

648

367

14

835

1,640

6,111

2,190

2,040

754

6,779

5,016

9,803

1,119

783

859

Production
(thousand metric tons)

Yield
(bushels/acre)

40
20

1,300

5,000,000 acres

Sown area   2,000,000 hectares

Scale 1:20,000,000

0   200   400 Miles

0   200   400 Kilometers

Gray tone represents zone of agriculture

*National average

Barley

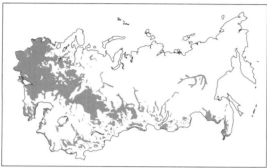

Barley is the most important Soviet feed grain in terms of both production and area. In the record-breaking 1973 harvest, barley accounted for more than one-half of the USSR's feed grain production, one-fourth of its total grain production, and 35 percent of the world barley crop. Most Soviet barley is used domestically; the small quantity entering foreign trade has had little impact on easing current world demand for feed grain.

Barley produces higher yields than other feed grains except corn. Consequently, more acreage is being devoted to it. An initial sharp rise in sown area occurred from 1960 to 1964, when the USSR shifted away from low-yielding oats and sown grasses. Recent increases in barley production reflect a further shift in crop emphasis, this time probably at the expense of rye. Increased planting and yield doubled production between 1965 and 1973—a major step toward expansion of the livestock industry.

Barley is grown principally in the south of European USSR but is adaptable to most agricultural regions. Primarily a spring grain, it is often sown in areas where winter grains are lost to winterkill.

Although used chiefly as a feed grain valued for its high nutritive content, barley is also used for human consumption. It is served extensively as *kasha* (grits or porridge) and occasionally is mixed with other flours for breadmaking. Barley is also a source of malt for distilleries and breweries.

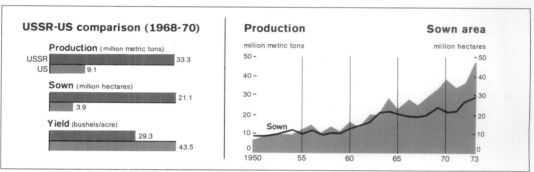

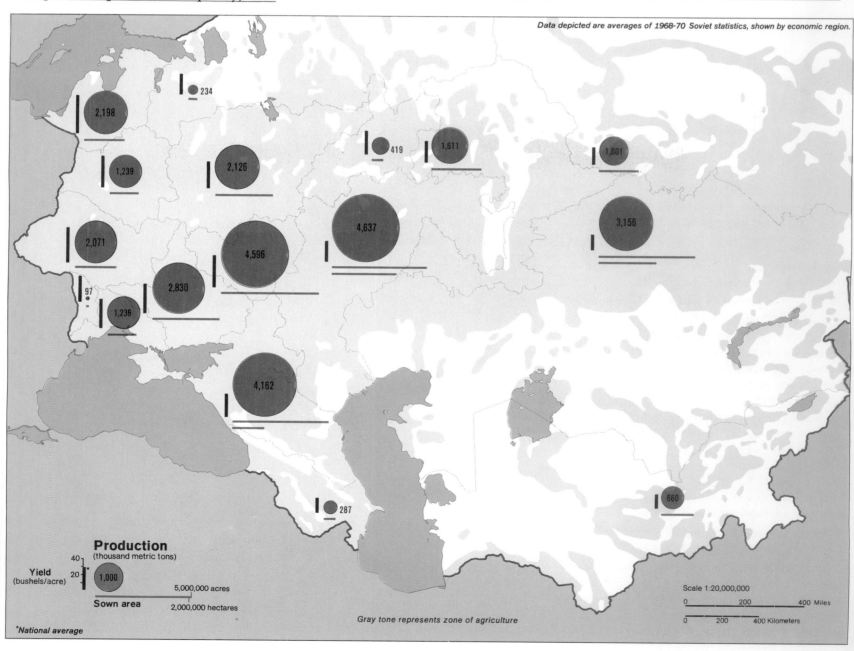

Data depicted are averages of 1968-70 Soviet statistics, shown by economic region.

Gray tone represents zone of agriculture

*National average

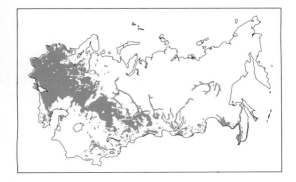

Oats

As the USSR's third largest grain crop, oats account for about 8 percent of all grain and 20 percent of feed grain production. In terms of world production, the USSR ranks first; however, oats are of little consequence in foreign trade.

Oat production over the past two decades correlates with the demand for oats as animal feed. In the 1950's, annual production ranged between 10 and 13.5 million tons; output fell rapidly in the early 1960's as tractors and trucks replaced draft animals and as oat feed was largely supplanted by more nutritive feed grains, corn and barley. The post-1963 increase in production resulted from the introduction of higher-yielding varieties and an expansion in sown hectarage to meet requirements of growing livestock herds. The oat harvest reached an all-time high of 17.4 million tons in 1973, although the planted area was even smaller than in the early 1950's.

The principal area sown to oats is in the cool, moist parts of central and northern European USSR and West Siberia, where the crop is grown on both chernozem and less fertile acid soils. Oats have an important role in the crop rotation pattern basic to the dairy/beef industry of these regions.

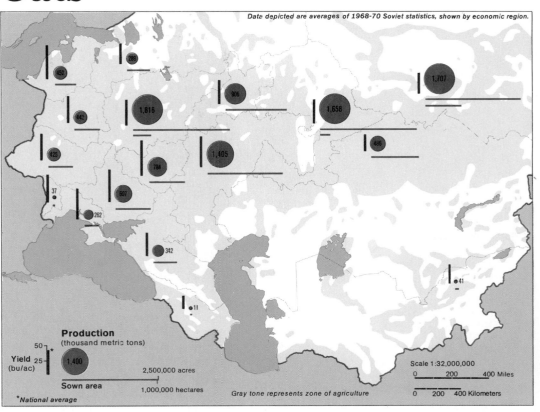

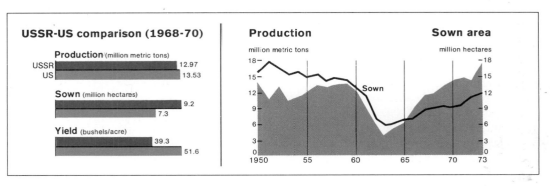

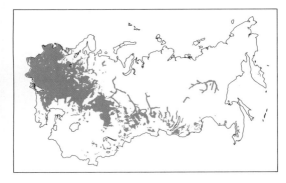

Rye

The significance of rye in Soviet agriculture has declined since the early 1950's; current production is only 55 percent of the 1951 high. However, in recent years rye has averaged 10 percent of Soviet food grain output, and the USSR continues to lead in world production. Paradoxically, it has imported rye in some years, including 1973.

The downward trend of production is attributable to the increasing popularity of wheat as a bread grain and to low government prices, especially since the mid-1960's. The area sown in rye is less than 30 percent of the 26 million hectares sown in 1951. It is grown principally in the northern regions of the USSR, where it is better adapted than other grains to the less fertile soils, and in the semiarid Volga region, where winter rye withstands early summer drought better than do spring sown crops.

Production may stabilize at 10 to 12 million tons, which generally meets current Soviet needs for rye and rye-wheat flour. On the other hand, increased demand for rye as a livestock feed, as it is used in some Western European countries, may result in increasing Soviet production.

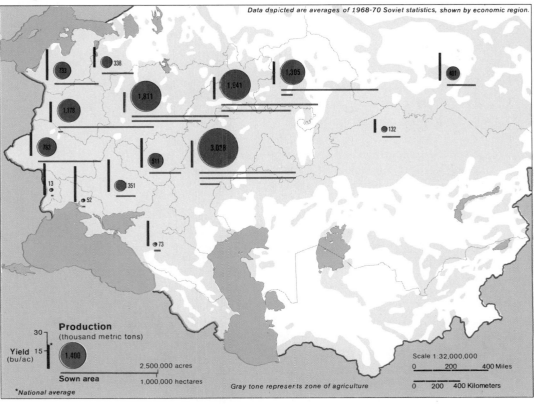

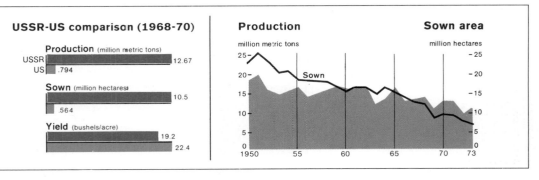

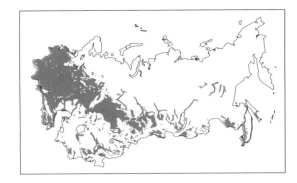

Corn

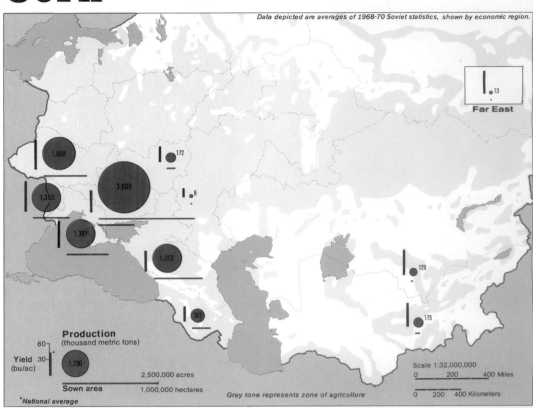

Corn is a much less important grain crop in the USSR than it is in the United States, primarily because climatic conditions are less favorable. Soviet production has averaged less than one-tenth of U.S. production in recent years. Even in 1973, when good weather and increased use of hybrid seed raised the average yield to 53 bushels per acre, corn accounted for only 6 percent of Soviet grain output.

Khrushchev's infatuation with "sausage on the stalk" during the late 1950's and early 1960's led to a sharp rise in the production of corn for grain, accomplished primarily by increasing the area sown. After Khrushchev's ouster, the corn program was sharply curtailed.

Much of the corn sown in the USSR fails to mature and is harvested for silage and green feed. In 1973, only 4 million of the 22 million hectares planted to corn produced fully matured corn grain. The principal corn grain area is in the southwestern USSR, but even there, growing conditions are less favorable than those in the U.S. Corn Belt. In parts of this same region, particularly in Moldavia, corn is a food staple as well as a feed grain.

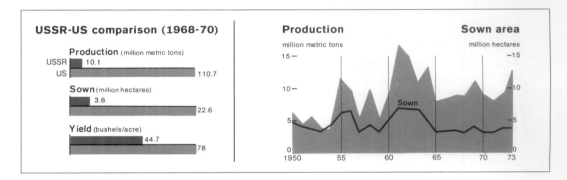

Rice

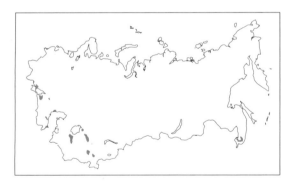

Rice, grown principally on the irrigated lands of the North Caucasus and Central Asia, is a minor but valuable food crop. Production in 1973 totaled 1.8 million tons, less than 2 percent of total food grain production. The current Five-Year Plan calls for a 1975 output of 2 million tons, which Soviet planners believe will meet domestic requirements.

Since 1960, rice output has increased sharply, primarily because of a fivefold expansion in sown area on irrigated land in Kuban' and, more recently, in Kazakhstan and southeastern Ukraine. Yields also have increased over the years. In 1973, the average yield was 1.5 tons per acre (3.8 tons per hectare), nearly double that of 1960. Ukrainian rice-growing areas averaged 2 tons per acre—comparable to U.S. yields—during 1966-70. Advanced tillage practices, heavier application of fertilizers, and good water management, characteristic of Ukrainian farms, contribute to the consistently higher yields.

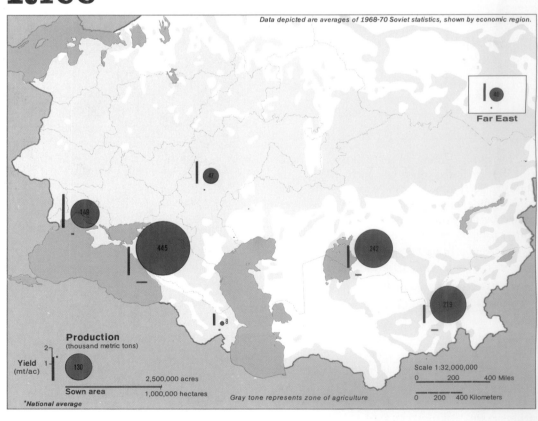

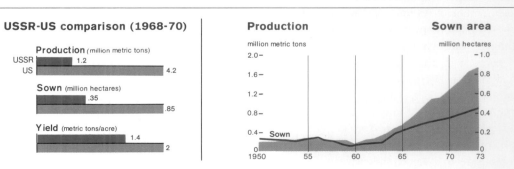

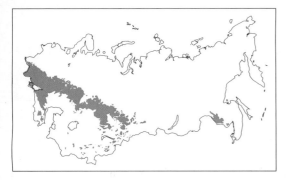

Sunflowers

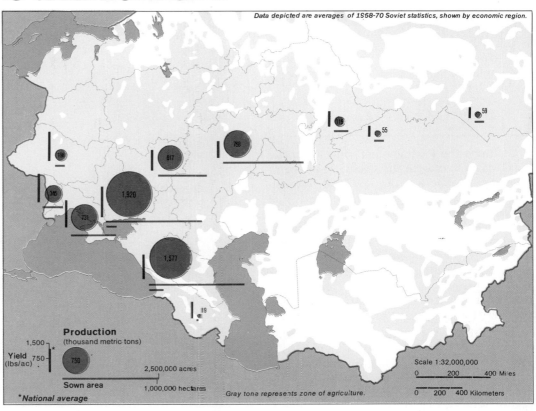

Sunflower seed is the source of three-fourths of the domestic production of vegetable oil in the USSR. In addition, roasted sunflower seeds are eaten much as peanuts are eaten elsewhere. The 1973 crop was a record 7.34 million tons, more than half of the world's output, and the average yield reached a new high of 1,374 pounds per acre (1,540 kg per hectare). During the period 1970-73, sunflower seed oil was the third largest Soviet agricultural export in terms of value. A residue oilseed cake is used for livestock feed.

Sunflowers take up almost a third of the area sown to industrial crops. Hardy and drought resistant, the sunflower plant is well suited to the southern regions of the USSR. Soviet varieties of sunflowers are the world's best in terms of oil content. Plant breeding for these characteristics, however, has reduced the protection afforded the seed kernel by the hull and thus increased the vulnerability of the seed to moisture and disease. This may be partly responsible for the declining yields in most recent years although poor weather clearly played a role.

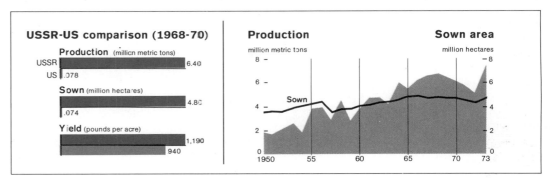

Sugar Beets

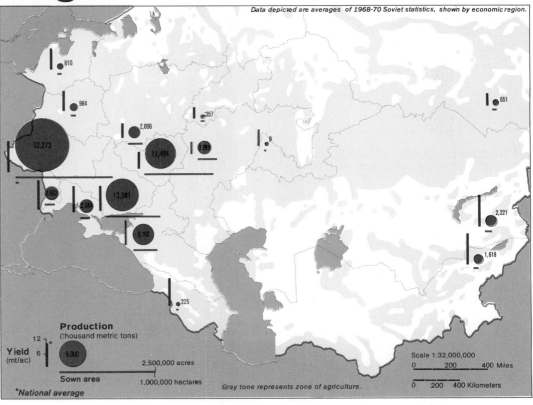

The USSR produces about one-third of the world's sugar beets. Although total production in 1973, an outstanding year, was 86.8 million tons, production in most recent years has fallen short of meeting the country's increasing sugar requirements. This reflects a decision to hold the sown area relatively constant and supplement domestic production with imports of Cuban raw sugar.

Yields are extremely responsive to weather and moisture fluctuation. Despite excellent growing conditions and increased fertilizer supplies in 1973, the average yield fell short of the 1968 record high of 10.8 tons per acre (26.6 tons per hectare). Yields are generally below those obtained in the United States and Europe because of lower fertilizer application rates and a tendency to plant later than the optimal time.

Sugar beet acreage is usually less than 2 percent of the total sown area. In 1973, 3.55 million hectares were planted—a slight increase over preceding years. However, a major increase in sugar beet plantings is restricted by the 4- to 6-year field rotation pattern necessary to reduce the plant's susceptibility to pest and disease problems.

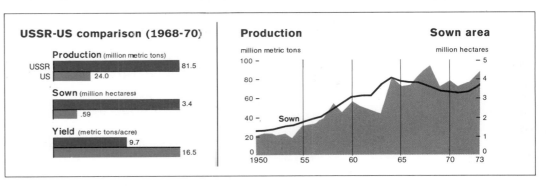

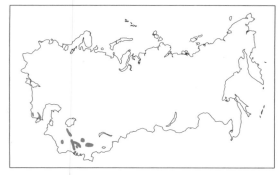

Cotton is the leading fiber crop and principal irrigated crop in the USSR. The record-breaking production of 7,662,000 tons in 1973 exceeded even the 1975 objective of the current Five-Year Plan. In 1967, 1970, and 1971, the USSR outproduced the United States and ranked first in world cotton production. Its share of total world production averaged approximately 19 percent for the 1970-73 period. Raw cotton is one of the two main Soviet agricultural exports, accounting for 15 percent of world exports.

Increases in production are attributable to some increases in sown area and significant increases in yields. Cotton yields nearly doubled between 1940 and 1960 and increased another 40 percent by 1973 to 2,490 pounds per acre (2,800 kilograms per hectare), far above the U.S. average. All Soviet cotton is grown under irrigation, a major factor accounting for the high yields; because of the crop's value, cotton fields probably receive priority when water supplies are low. Central Asia produces more than 90 percent of the country's cotton, and Azerbaijan supplies most of the remainder. These are the only major areas in the USSR that have the high temperatures and long growing season needed.

Cotton

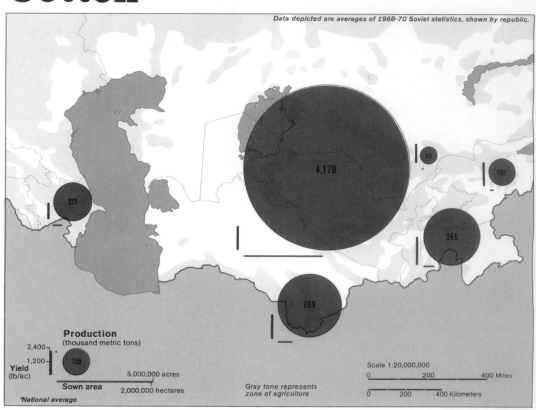

Data depicted are averages of 1968-70 Soviet statistics, shown by republic.

Production (thousand metric tons)

Yield (lb/ac)
*National average

5,000,000 acres
Sown area
2,000,000 hectares

Gray tone represents zone of agriculture

Scale 1:20,000,000
0   200   400 Miles
0   200   400 Kilometers

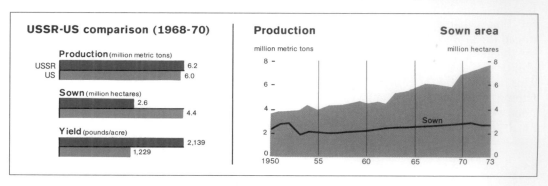

USSR-US comparison (1968-70)

Production (million metric tons)
USSR 6.2
US 6.0

Sown (million hectares)
2.6
4.4

Yield (pounds/acre)
2,139
1,229

Production
million metric tons

Sown area
million hectares

Sown

Flax (for fiber)

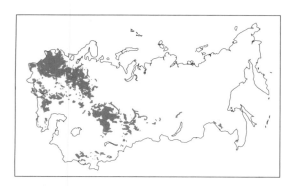

The USSR produces two-thirds of the world's flax for fiber. Some seed flax is also grown for linseed oil, used in the manufacture of paints and varnishes. In contrast, United States flax production is almost totally for the seed.

Although the area planted to flax for fiber has declined from 1.9 million hectares in 1950 to 1.2 million in 1973, increased yields have nearly doubled production since 1950. Average production during 1970-73 dropped to 460,000 tons, chiefly because of bad weather. However, the Soviet Union accounts for 10 to 15 percent of world flax-fiber exports.

Flax is widely grown in the temperate zone of the USSR; the principal flax-fiber producing area is northwestern European USSR, where the cool, moist climate is conducive to plant development and to the process of removing the fiber from the wood. Although it is nutrient exhausting and requires heavy fertilization of the regionally poor soils, flax is a good cash crop, and it complements the dairy/beef economy of the region.

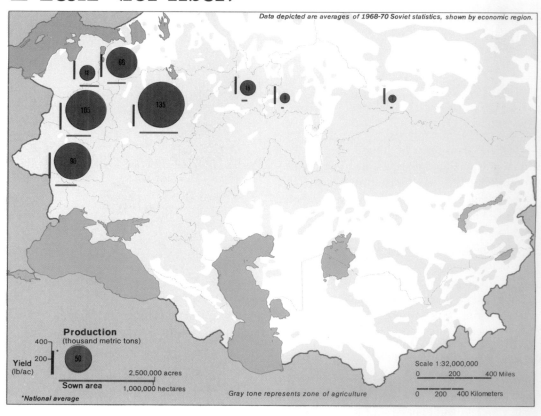

Data depicted are averages of 1968-70 Soviet statistics, shown by economic region.

Production (thousand metric tons)

Yield (lb/ac)
*National average

2,500,000 acres
Sown area
1,000,000 hectares

Gray tone represents zone of agriculture

Scale 1:32,000,000
0   200   400 Miles
0   200   400 Kilometers

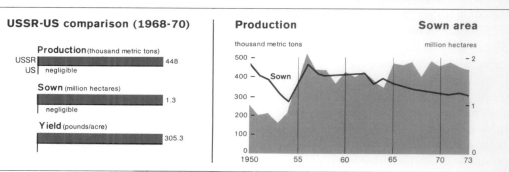

USSR-US comparison (1968-70)

Production (thousand metric tons)
USSR 448
US negligible

Sown (million hectares)
1.3
negligible

Yield (pounds/acre)
305.3

Production
thousand metric tons

Sown area
million hectares

Sown

Other Crops

Potatoes. The USSR is the world's leading potato producer. Potatoes, called a "second bread," are the most important Soviet food crop after grains and are also used for animal feed and as raw material for industrial products. The 1973 harvest of 108 million tons was 23 percent of the total value of Soviet crop production. By contrast, potatoes average only 3 percent of the total U.S. output.

Increased yields have enabled Soviet production to rise during the past two decades despite a drop in sown area. Very favorable growing conditions during 1973 resulted in yields one-half ton per acre higher than the average of recent years. Although potatoes grow in all agricultural regions of the country, they thrive best in the friable, well drained soils of the cool, moist western and central regions of European USSR. The highest average yields, 6.5 tons per acre (16 tons per hectare), are obtained in the Baltic Region.

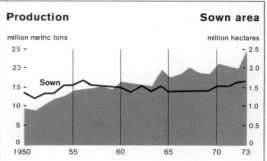

Vegetables. Beets, cabbages, carrots, cucumbers, onions, and tomatoes account for most Soviet vegetable production. These same six account for about one-third of the more varied U.S. vegetable crop. Approximately 24.5 million tons of vegetables were harvested in the USSR in 1973, with the average yield for all vegetables a record 6 tons per acre (14.8 tons per hectare).

Soviet vegetable plantings have ranged between 1.4 and 1.6 million hectares for the past decade, less than 1 percent of the total sown area. A small but increasing portion of irrigated land is being sown in vegetables, especially in the environs of major urban centers.

The absence of sweet corn, beans, and such leafy vegetables as lettuce and spinach is attributable to both environment and eating habits. Favorite hothouse crops, especially in the Arctic, are cucumbers and tomatoes.

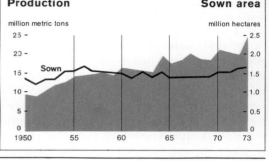

Fruit. Fruit production has averaged about 7.4 million tons in recent years, more than a threefold increase over the 1950 output. Although yields have improved, the increase in output results primarily from a substantial expansion in orchard area. Fruit trees are also being planted to form local windbreaks. Hardy fruits such as apples and pears are grown in the temperate northern areas, and plums and apricots in the warmer areas. Citrus, most vulnerable to frosts, is restricted to the coastal areas of the Transcaucasus.

Both table and wine grapes are grown in the warm southern republics of the USSR. Moldavia, the Ukraine, and the Transcaucasus account for nearly three-fourths of the production and a like percentage of vineyard hectarage. Yields increased sharply during the 1960's and now average about 1.5 tons per acre (3.7 tons per hectare), due largely to an increase in the density of vines and the planting of improved, disease resistant varieties. The 1971 grape production of 4.5 million tons was more than double that of 1960, although vineyard acreage has remained about 1.1 million hectares.

Tea. *Chay,* the Russian word for tea, probably is a derivative of the Cantonese *ch'a.* Tea cultivation was introduced into Russia in the mid-1800's and during the 1930's expanded substantially to 55,300 hectares. Since World War II, the area of cultivation has grown further to approximately 76,000 hectares, almost all of it located in those parts of the Georgian Republic where there is a warm moist climate and an abundance of labor. Expanded use of leaf-picking machinery has helped increase Soviet tea production to a record 305,000 tons in 1973, a 55 percent gain over 1967. Despite these advances, supplemental imports are needed to meet domestic requirements. Tea cultivation has not been practiced in the United States since the late 1890's because of high labor costs.

Soybeans. Soybeans in the USSR constitute about 12 percent of the total vegetable oilseed crop. Harvests over the past 5 years ranged from 260,000 to 603,000 tons, with the 1973 output, 423,000 tons, representing a sharp recovery from the previous year's low. Production is limited by both low yields and a small sown area. Yields in 1973 averaged 7.5 bushels per acre (18.5 bushels per hectare), a figure Soviet growers expect to improve through the use of herbicides, lime, and new varieties that can withstand the vagaries of weather. The sown area of 838,000 hectares in 1973, although three times greater than in 1940, remained a negligible percentage of Soviet sown land. Almost all soybean cultivation is in the Soviet Far East, principally in Amur Oblast, where best yields are obtained on reclaimed swampland soils. Plans call for increased planting in the Ukraine and in Kazakhstan, where intense research is under way to develop varieties adaptable to local conditions.

Millet and buckwheat. Millet and buckwheat production in 1973 totaled 5.7 million tons, only 2.5 percent of the total grain output but much larger than harvests of the preceding decade. Millet yielded an exceptional 28 bushels per acre (69 bushels per hectare), double the previous average annual yield. Both are primarily food crops, although they are also used as livestock feed. Buckwheat is also an excellent source of nectar, vital to apiculture. The area sown to millet and buckwheat has declined in recent years as emphasis was placed on higher-yield crops. It may stabilize at 4 to 5 million hectares since each has value as an insurance crop—one that matures within a short period and is susceptible to few insect pests or diseases. Millet, relatively drought resistant, is sown principally in the spring wheat belt of the Volga and Ural steppes and in the North Caucasus. Buckwheat, which is sensitive to drought, is cultivated primarily on the less fertile soils too moist for other grains in central European USSR.

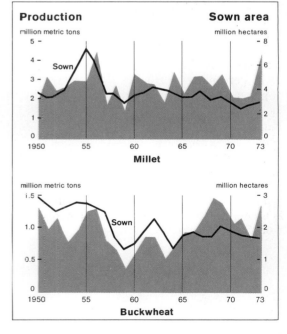

Livestock

Increased output of livestock products is one of the foremost objectives of Soviet agriculture. Although meat production has increased over the past decade, it still falls short of consumer requirements. The ambitious goals of the current Five-Year Plan (1971-75) to raise production of meat by 30 percent, milk by 20 percent, eggs by 28 percent, and wool by 19 percent received a temporary setback from the poor harvest of 1972. The goals may be met, however, given continued Soviet efforts to achieve more mechanization, better structuring of cattle herds, and improvement of the feed supply.

The advantages of specialized breeds and improved technology are only beginning to be realized in the USSR, and productivity per animal in livestock products is still relatively low. The average milk yield per cow in the USSR is about half that of the United States although total Soviet milk production has been higher since 1958. Almost all cows in the USSR are milked while only about one-fourth of all U.S. cows, especially bred and fed to produce high milk yields, are used for dairy purposes. Soviet meat production is

about two-thirds of U.S. output despite almost equal numbers of cattle and swine, again indicating lower productivity rates for the USSR. Average production tends to be slightly lower for animals of kolkhozes and sovkhozes than for privately owned livestock.

The USSR plans to achieve production increases through the use of numerous large mechanized livestock complexes for cattle, swine, and poultry. Hopes ride high that productivity will also be substantially increased by the employment of more efficient techniques on existing sovkhozes and kolkhozes.

The livestock feed base is being improved by increasing the amount of land sown in fodder crops and by enlarging the area of natural pasturelands through drainage and irrigation. Clover and alfalfa are the main perennial grasses, while corn silage provides much of the succulent fodder. A drive is currently under way to increase productivity by the use of new machinery for harvesting fodder crops and improved methods of storage. Also, production of high protein feeds— such as fish and bone meals, nutrient yeast,

and phosphates—is being drastically increased during the current Five-Year Plan.

The USSR cattle population has generally increased during the last decade, although a brief downturn followed the poor 1963 grain crop, and a small reduction in the availability of feed per animal caused another reduction in 1969 and 1970. Beef production reflects these dips. The swine population, which shows more pronounced fluctuations in response to changing crop production, declined drastically at the end of 1963 and did not regain pre-1963 levels until 1972. Similarly, shortages of feed also caused a sharp drop in poultry numbers in 1963, the effects of which were felt until 1969. Poultry raising in large complexes is being pushed during the current Five-Year Plan, and a continued increase in numbers is likely. Sheep and goats, largely pasture-fed, are only slightly affected by crop variations, and their numbers have remained fairly constant for the past decade. Increases will come from improvements in pasturelands and, to a lesser degree, from the addition of a few large mechanized farms.

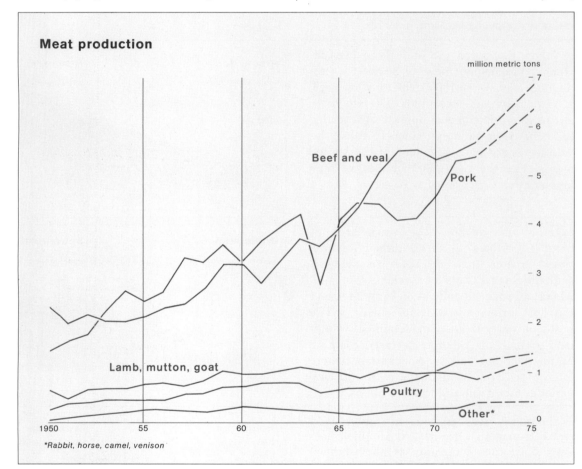

Meat production

million metric tons

Beef and veal

Pork

Lamb, mutton, goat

Poultry

Other*

1950   55   60   65   70   75

*Rabbit, horse, camel, venison

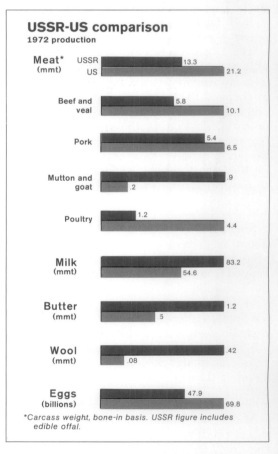

USSR-US comparison
1972 production

Meat* (mmt)	USSR	13.3
	US	21.2
Beef and veal		5.8
		10.1
Pork		5.4
		6.5
Mutton and goat		.2
		.9
Poultry		1.2
		4.4
Milk (mmt)		83.2
		54.6
Butter (mmt)		1.2
		5
Wool (mmt)		.42
		.08
Eggs (billions)		47.9
		69.8

*Carcass weight, bone-in basis. USSR figure includes edible offal.

Complex built to house 108,000 pigs

The distribution of meat-producing animals in the USSR follows the distribution of population, unlike the situation in the United States where livestock tend to be concentrated in less populous states. Most Soviet cows are utilized for both beef and milk, and the dairy industry everywhere is population oriented; in addition, the Soviet livestock industry has been labor-intensive and thus well suited to areas of dense rural settlement.

Feed supply and climate also affect livestock distribution. Half of the country is too cold for livestock other than yaks or reindeer. Vast dry areas, particularly in Kazakhstan and Central Asia, are suited only to sheep and goat pasturage. In less arid parts of Kazakhstan the area of natural pasture required to support one head of cattle is about 10 hectares, whereas in the Central Chernozem Region and the Ukraine it is only about 1 hectare. Beef and dairy cattle, as well as swine and poultry, are therefore concentrated in the agricultural west, where a rich variety of fodder crops—clover, alfalfa, corn silage—can be grown.

Wastes from food industries, also located primarily in western USSR, provide additional sources of livestock feed. Swine and poultry in particular utilize this type of nourishment. Sugar beet factories are among the leading sources, and waste from alcohol, dairy, oil, meat, fish, and milling plants is also important. Food garbage from large urban areas is used extensively for swine—as much as 40 percent of feed—on sovkhozes near large cities in western USSR.

The construction of large industrialized complexes for livestock will tend to increase concentration of meat production near large population centers. The relative importance of seminomadic herding in the eastern parts of the country will then decline even further.

Number of livestock

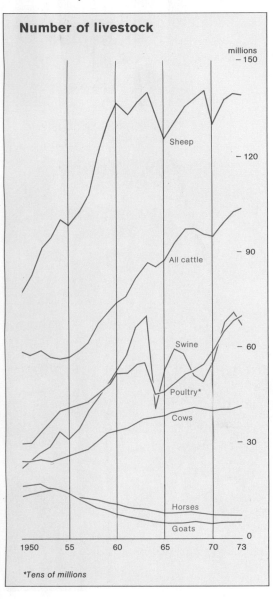

Cattle

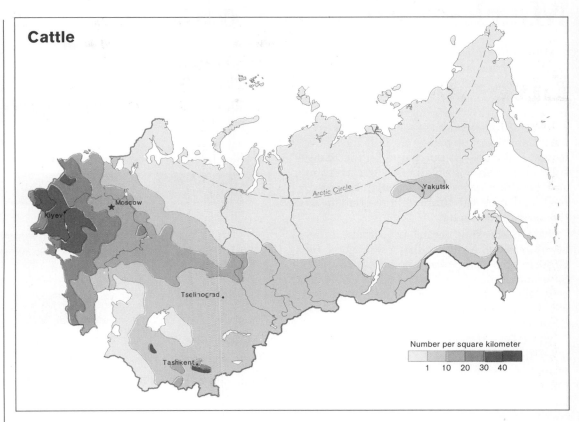

Number per square kilometer

1 10 20 30 40

Swine

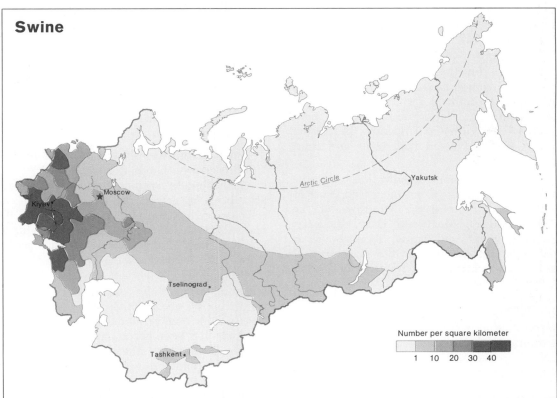

Number per square kilometer

1 10 20 30 40

Sheep and goats

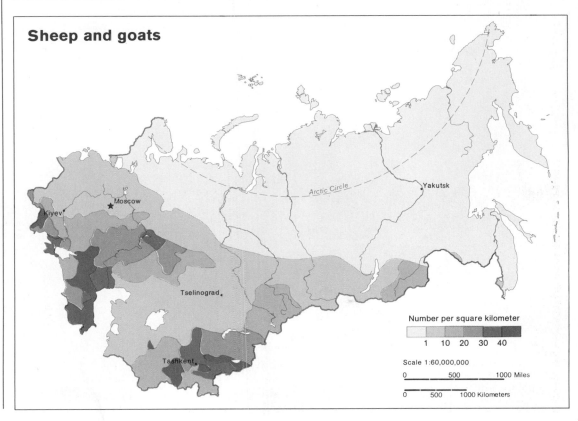

Number per square kilometer

1 10 20 30 40

Scale 1:60,000,000

0   500   1000 Miles

0   500   1000 Kilometers

Marketing and Consumption

Most agricultural products in the USSR reach the consumer via the State procurement system, but there also exists a lively and extensive market in "surplus" produce through collective farm markets. Almost 100 percent of some products—such as raw cotton, flax fiber, sugar beets, tobacco, tea leaves, and wool—is purchased by the State; substantial portions of others, such as grain and potatoes—which are needed for seed, feed, and personal consumption—remain in the agricultural sector.

State purchasing organs have fixed delivery quotas for each product established by Gosplan, the state planning administration. Substantial premiums—as much as 50 percent above the base price—are paid for above-plan purchases of grain, sugar beets, livestock products, and some vegetables.

The USSR Ministry of Procurement organizes the acquisition by the Government of all types of agricultural materials, supervises the fulfillment of procurement plans, and is largely responsible for food inspection. It coordinates the work of other ministries and departments which purchase agricultural products and defines the zones or areas in which they may operate.

The Ministry of Procurement is directly responsible for the purchase, storage, and proper utilization of state grain resources. It maintains centralized grain drying and storage facilities (on-farm grain storage is managed by the farm) and operates processing plants such as mixed feed mills and flour mills.

Other purchasing organizations are the Central Union of Consumer Cooperatives (Tsentrosoyuz), and the Ministries of the Food Industry, Meat and Dairy Industry, Light Industry, and Trade. Tsentrosoyuz is an important channel for the marketing of some livestock products, potatoes and other vegetables, and fruit. In 1970, for example, it procured all the eggs and wool purchased by the Government. It buys not only from farms but also from individuals who have surplus output from their personal plots.

Collective farm market

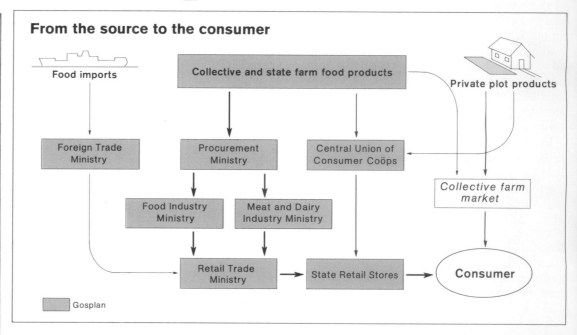

From the source to the consumer

State and collective farms have the option of marketing surplus products through the collective farm markets which exist in all cities and in nearly every town and village. Prices in these markets are relatively free to respond to supply and demand, and the prospect of higher prices attracts surplus farm production. As a result, the collective farm market is an important source of supply, particularly for urban residents who frequently cannot purchase good quality fruit, vegetables, and meat in the state retail trade network.

The availability and variety of food in the USSR is greater than in the past, and the consumer has made significant gains. There has also been a marked shift away from a reliance on home-produced foods. By 1970, more than 80 percent of the collective farm families' food was purchased at state retail stores and farm markets.

Although the Soviet diet is still heavily weighted with starchy foods, it has improved significantly since 1950. Growth in consumption of high quality foods, such as livestock products, has been accompanied by a reduction in the number of calories supplied by grain and potatoes.

The Soviet distribution and marketing systems have been improved, although large cities are still favored in overall distribution. Processing, packaging, and storage of food have been expanded but are not yet near U.S. levels. Thus, produce is far less subject to seasonal fluctuations than before and more canned goods are available.

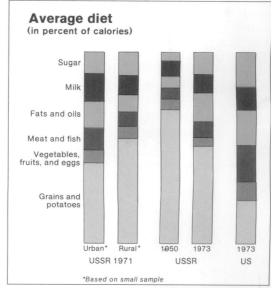

Average diet
(in percent of calories)

Sugar
Milk
Fats and oils
Meat and fish
Vegetables, fruits, and eggs
Grains and potatoes

Urban*   Rural*   1950   1973   1973
USSR 1971   USSR   US

*Based on small sample

Weights and Measures

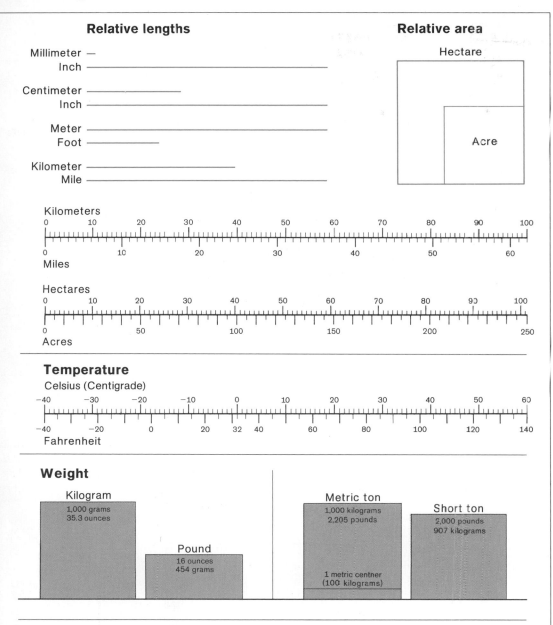

Relative lengths

Millimeter —
Inch
Centimeter
Inch
Meter
Foot
Kilometer
Mile

Relative area

Hectare

Acre

Kilometers
0   10   20   30   40   50   60   70   80   90   100

0   10   20   30   40   50   60
Miles

Hectares
0   10   20   30   40   50   60   70   80   90   100

0   50   100   150   200   250
Acres

Temperature

Celsius (Centigrade)
−40   −30   −20   −10   0   10   20   30   40   50   60

−40   −20   0   20   32   40   60   80   100   120   140
Fahrenheit

Weight

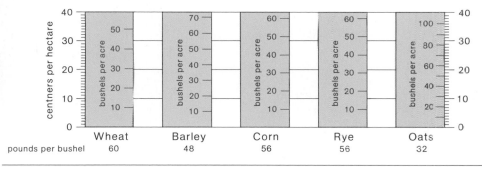

Kilogram
1,000 grams
35.3 ounces

Pound
16 ounces
454 grams

Metric ton
1,000 kilograms
2,205 pounds

1 metric centner
(100 kilograms)

Short ton
2,000 pounds
907 kilograms

Yield conversions for major crops

centners per hectare: 0, 10, 20, 30, 40

Wheat (bushels per acre 10–50)
Barley (bushels per acre 10–70)
Corn (bushels per acre 10–60)
Rye (bushels per acre 10–60)
Oats (bushels per acre 20–100)

pounds per bushel: Wheat 60, Barley 48, Corn 56, Rye 56, Oats 32

Conversion table for major crops

To convert	Metric tons to bushels	Bushels to metric tons	Centners per hectare to bushels per acre	Bushels per acre to centners per hectare
		Multiply by:		
Wheat & potatoes	36.743	.02722	1.487	.6725
Rye & corn	39.368	.02540	1.593	6277
Barley	45.929	.02177	1.859	.5380
Oats	68.894	.01452	2.788	.3587

Conversions from metric measures

Symbol	When you know	Multiply by	To find	Symbol
mm	millimeters	.039	inches	in
cm	centimeters	.394	inches	in
m	meters	3.281	feet	ft
m	meters	1.094	yards	yd
km	kilometers	.621	miles	mi
cm^2	square centimeters	.155	square inches	in^2
m^2	square meters	1.196	square yards	yd^2
km^2	square kilometers	.386	square miles	mi^2
ha	hectares	2.471	acres	ac
kg	kilograms	2.205	pounds	lb
mt	metric tons	1.102	short tons	sht

Money

Rubles to dollars

One ruble is equivalent to $1.32 at the official exchange rate in 1974. However, since Soviet prices are set arbitrarily by central planners and do not reflect world prices or domestic supply and demand conditions, they are not an accurate measure of resources needed to produce goods and services.

Administrative Divisions

58